THE STORY ATLAS
OF THE BIBLE

ELROSE HUNTER

ANDROMEDA

Illustrated by

Mike Foster *(Maltings Partnership)*
Julian Baker
Adam Hook, Roger Payne, Clive Spong *(Linden Artists)*
Richard Berridge, Julia Pearson *(Specs Art)*
Mark Viney *(Allied Artists)*
Tony Smith *(Virgil Pomfret Agency)*

Consultant editor : Judith Merrell

This edition printed exclusively for
Scholastic Publications Limited 1994

Planned and produced by
Andromeda Oxford Limited
11–15 The Vineyard
Abingdon
Oxon
OX14 3PX

ISBN 1 871869 34 X
Printed in Slovenia

CONTENTS

THE WORLD OF THE BIBLE   4

LONG AGO WHEN THE WORLD BEGAN   8

ABRAHAM AND THE PROMISED LAND   10

JACOB AND ESAU: THE SHEPHERD AND THE HUNTER   12

JOSEPH THE DREAMER   14

MOSES: THE SLAVE WHO BECAME A PRINCE   16

FORTY YEARS TO CROSS THE DESERT   18

JOSHUA THE GREAT COMMANDER   20

GIDEON: A MIGHTY HERO   22

RUTH AND NAOMI'S TREK   24

SAMUEL AND SAUL: WISE AND FOOLISH LEADERS   26

DAVID: ISRAEL'S GREATEST KING   28

SOLOMON'S TEMPLE   30

CARGOES OF IVORY, GOLD AND MONKEYS   32

DIVIDED LOYALTIES: GOD OR BAAL?   34

JONAH, THE RELUCTANT PROPHET   36

WAR AND EXILE   38

DANIEL, GOD'S FAITHFUL SERVANT   40

NEHEMIAH REBUILDS JERUSALEM   42

LOOKING BACKWARDS AND FORWARDS   44

THE SAVIOUR BORN IN A STABLE   46

JOHN THE BAPTIST PREPARES FOR JESUS   48

JESUS AT WORK IN GALILEE   50

A WARM WELCOME AT JERUSALEM   52

TREACHERY IN JERUSALEM   54

JESUS CONQUERS DEATH   56

GOOD NEWS FOR THE WORLD   58

TURN-ABOUT ON THE DAMASCUS ROAD   60

PAUL'S MISSIONARY ADVENTURES   62

INDEX   64

THE WORLD OF THE BIBLE

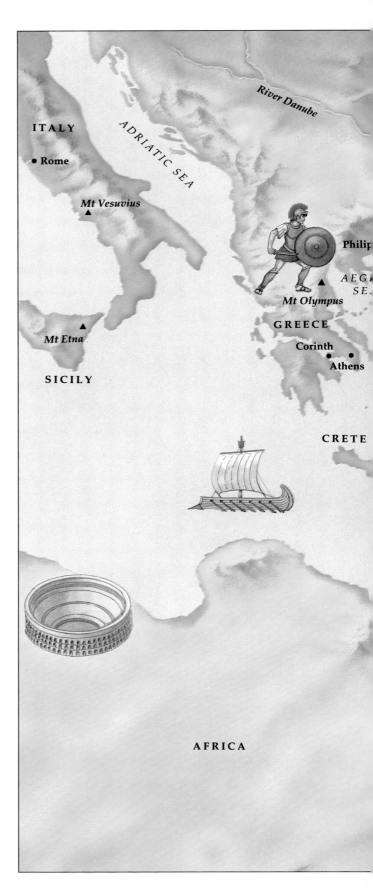

I F WE FOLLOW the Bible story from when the world began to Paul's travels to spread the Christian faith, we are taken on a long journey over thousands of miles – westward from the Middle East to the lands that surround the Mediterranean Sea. It may not look a large area when we see it on our world map today, but to people of the time, well over two thousand years ago, travel over these lands was much slower so the distances seemed vast.

We are also going on a journey back in time because the events in the Bible stretch back over four thousand years.

MEDITERRANEAN WORLD

The events in the Bible took place around the Mediterranean and in the Middle East (above). This part of the world was the centre of civilisation in Bible times. During the history of the Old and New Testaments, five nations in turn became powerful empires: the Assyrians, the Babylonians, the Persians, the Greeks and the Romans (right).

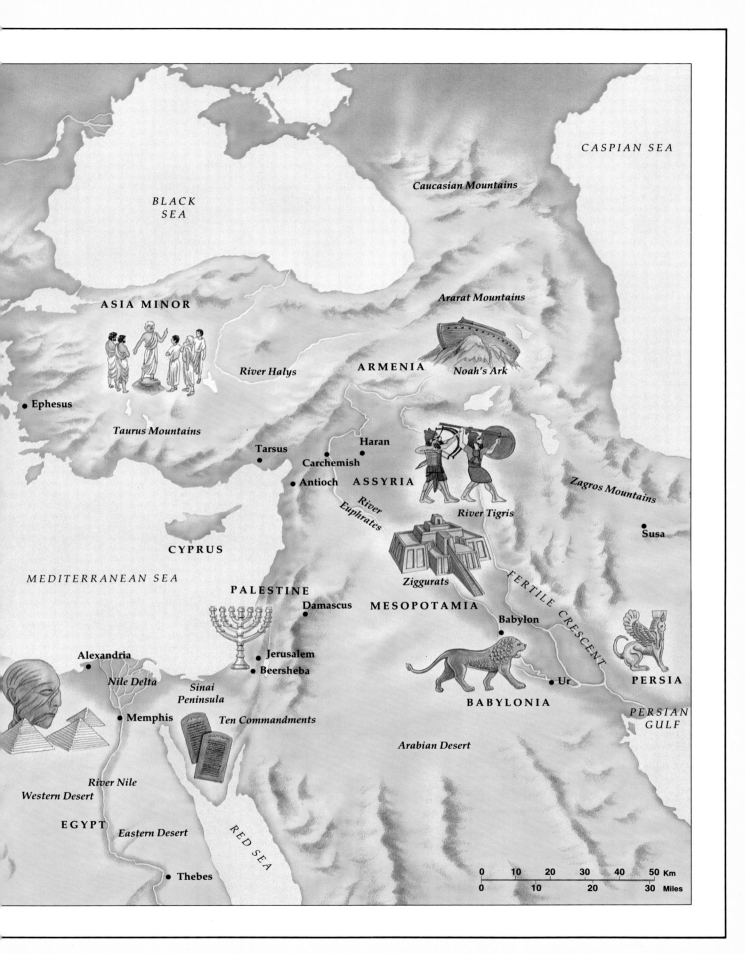

CASPIAN SEA

BLACK
SEA

Caucasian Mountains

ASIA MINOR

Ararat Mountains

ARMENIA   *Noah's Ark*

River Halys

● **Ephesus**

Taurus Mountains

● **Tarsus**

Haran ●

Carchemish

Zagros Mountains

● **Antioch**   ASSYRIA

*River
Euphrates*

River Tigris

● **Susa**

CYPRUS

Ziggurats

MEDITERRANEAN SEA

PALESTINE

Damascus ●   MESOPOTAMIA

FERTILE CRESCENT

● **Alexandria**

● **Jerusalem**

● **Beersheba**

Babylon
●

● **Ur**

PERSIA

Nile Delta

*Sinai
Peninsula*

BABYLONIA

PERSIAN
GULF

● **Memphis**

Ten Commandments

Arabian Desert

River Nile

Western Desert

EGYPT   *Eastern Desert*

RED SEA

● **Thebes**

0	10	20	30	40	50 Km
0		10		20		30	Miles

OUR BIBLE JOURNEY

Our journey begins in Mesopotamia, a land sometimes called the 'Cradle of Civilisation'. The fertile lands fed by two rivers, the Tigris and Euphrates, made it possible for people to settle there, grow crops and build cities.

We set out with Abraham from the city of Ur about 2000 BC and travel the 'Fertile Crescent' to the land of Canaan. Abraham, and his descendants Isaac and Jacob, were nomads in Canaan: this meant they lived in tents and moved from place to place in search of water and pasture for their flocks of sheep and goats. God promised Abraham that the land of Canaan would belong to his descendants and the country became known as the 'Promised Land'.

From Canaan we travel south to Egypt. We arrive there with Joseph who starts off as a slave and ends up becoming the Pharaoh's governor. The pyramids had been built about a thousand years earlier and Egypt had a long history of civilisation.

We stay in Egypt for several hundred years. During this time the descendants of Joseph become the nation of Israelites. They are made slaves by the Egyptians. Shortly after the time of Tutankhamun, Moses is born. He is to rescue the Israelites and lead them away from Egypt across the desert back to the Promised Land.

When they eventually enter the land and capture the first city, Jericho, it is the start of a long period of conquest. The Canaanites and the Philistines, already in the land, have to be conquered and driven out.

By 1000 BC, King David and King Solomon have extended the Israelites' territory, and for a time there is peace. But then a shadow creeps slowly across from the east as the mighty empires of first Assyria, and then Babylonia, grow stronger and seize more lands.

We journey on from the ruins of Jerusalem in 586 BC with thousands of prisoners of war, like Daniel, into exile in Babylonia. After seventy years when the exiles are allowed to return home, we go back to Jerusalem and see Nehemiah organise the rebuilding of the city.

We end our Old Testament journey with the land of Israel becoming part of the Greek Empire, when Alexander the Great conquers the civilised world.

After a gap of about three hundred years, we take up our travels into the New Testament when the Romans have made Palestine part of their Empire. Augustus is emperor when Jesus is born in Bethlehem.

We follow in the footsteps of Jesus, staying within the land of Palestine. We journey with him around the towns and villages of Galilee where we see him teaching and healing.

Modern Israel and the Near East

We head south with Jesus to Jerusalem where he is arrested, tried and put to death. We finally follow his disciples taking the gospel beyond the borders of Palestine (notably Paul as far as Europe), after Jesus has risen.

PROMISED LAND: OLD AND NEW

The land known by various names in its history as Canaan, the Promised Land, Israel and Palestine, is the setting for most of our stories. It occupies a key position linking Africa and Asia like a bridge. But it is a small country – only

about 175 miles from north to south, and about half that distance from west to east. There are four main geographical regions: the Coastal Plain, Central Highlands, Jordan Rift Valley and Eastern Plateau. The map of the same area (below, left) shows locations today.

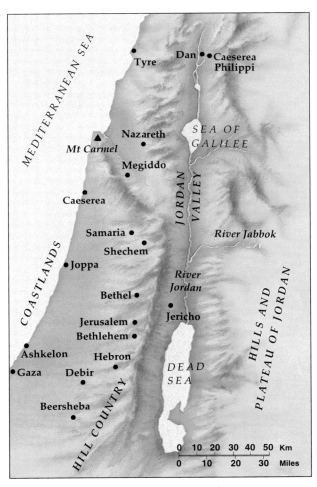

TRAVEL IN THE BIBLE WORLD

In Bible times most land journeys were on foot or on the backs of animals such as donkeys and camels. Wooden-wheeled wagons pulled by donkeys or oxen were used as early as the time of Abraham. Horses appeared later, but were owned only by kings and warriors. King Solomon had stables for several thousand horses. The horse was used mainly for pulling war chariots.

Roads were developed as empires grew. The Persian kings built the Royal Road from their capital city of Susa west for 1600 miles to the city of Sardis in Asia Minor. They organised a system of posting stations, placing horses and messengers a day's journey apart all along the road. Official letters could be handed down the line and took only three weeks to deliver between Susa and Sardis.

But it was the Romans who set up the greatest network of roads in Bible lands, right across their empire.

By the first century after Jesus' death, many people moved freely across the Roman empire. This helped Paul and others to found Christian churches in Asia Minor and Europe and to keep in touch by letter.

Most of the lands of the Bible border the Mediterranean Sea. There was travel too by water from the earliest times. The Egyptians sailed up and down the River Nile and also built sea-going ships for travel across the Mediterranean. Over a thousand years before Jesus, the Phoenicians, who lived on the coast north of Palestine, were adventurous sailors and explored westwards to Europe and south around Africa.

The Israelites were not really sea-faring people, partly because their coastline has no safe, natural harbours. It was not until Roman times, when a harbour was built at Caesarea, that regular trade by sea was established.

LONG AGO WHEN THE WORLD BEGAN

GENESIS 1–11

I**N THE** beginning, when God created Adam and Eve, he planted a beautiful garden for them to enjoy. A stream watered the Garden of Eden and all kinds of flowers and trees grew there.

Adam and Eve tended the garden and ate the fruit from the trees. But God told them not to eat the fruit of one particular tree. One day they disobeyed God and ate the fruit. So he sent them away from the Garden of Eden. From then on Adam and Eve had to work hard to grow food for themselves as well as their family.

The ark was made of wood and coated with tar

NOAH'S ARK

Noah built an ark 150m long, 25m wide and 15m high. He took two of every kind of animal on board the ark, to survive the flood.

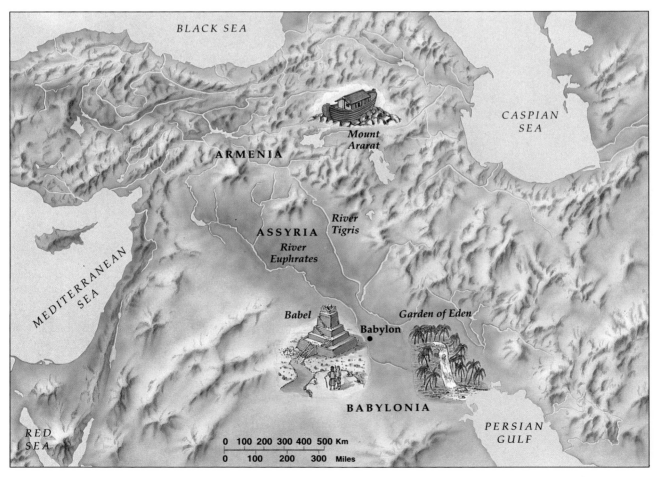

BLACK SEA

CASPIAN SEA

ARMENIA

Mount Ararat

River Tigris

ASSYRIA

River Euphrates

MEDITERRANEAN SEA

Babel

Babylon

Garden of Eden

BABYLONIA

RED SEA

PERSIAN GULF

0 100 200 300 400 500 Km
0   100   200   300   Miles

Many years passed and the number of people on the Earth grew. They ignored God and became evil and violent. God was sorry that he had put them on the Earth and he decided to start again. But he made an agreement with a good man, Noah, that he would keep him and his family alive, and also two of every kind of animal.

Noah followed God's instructions and built a great boat. When it was ready and all were on board, rain fell for forty days and forty nights. Only those on the boat survived the flood that covered the land.

As the flood waters went down, the boat came to rest on Mount Ararat. When Noah and his family and all the animals left the boat, God made a rainbow appear in the sky. It was a sign of his promise that he would never again destroy the world by a flood.

Noah's sons – Shem, Ham and Japheth – became the ancestors of all the nations of the world. Years passed and the descendants of Noah settled on a plain in Babylonia. They had discovered how to make bricks with mud and tar and they decided to build a city with a tower to reach the sky. 'If we do this, we will become famous,' they said.

God looked at their tower. 'These people think they do not need me,' God said and he mixed up their language so they could not understand each other and could not build the city together. God scattered the people with their new languages across the Earth. The Tower of Babel was never finished.

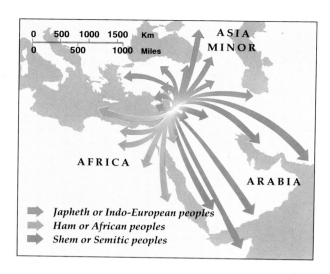

GROWTH OF THE NATIONS

Noah's sons and their descendants spread out to fill the world with many different peoples (above).

THE TOWER OF BABEL

God punished the people for building the tower by jumbling their language, so they could not talk to each other (below).

IN THE BEGINNING

God created the Garden of Eden and filled it with all kinds of plants and creatures. The land was extremely fertile and was watered by rivers including the Tigris and Euphrates (left).

ABRAHAM AND THE PROMISED LAND

GENESIS 11–24

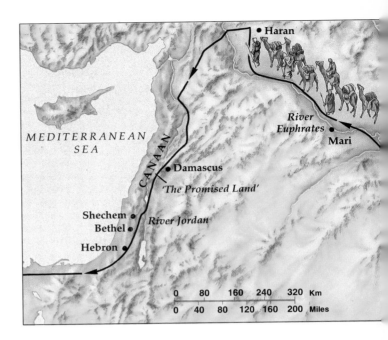

ABRAHAM WAS born in the city of Ur in Mesopotamia about 2,000 years before the time of Jesus. The people of Ur lived in mud-brick houses, traded with far-off lands and worshipped the Moon god.

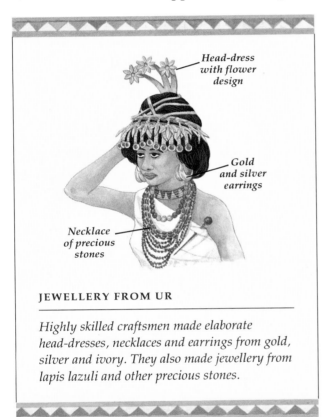

Head-dress with flower design

Gold and silver earrings

Necklace of precious stones

JEWELLERY FROM UR

Highly skilled craftsmen made elaborate head-dresses, necklaces and earrings from gold, silver and ivory. They also made jewellery from lapis lazuli and other precious stones.

THE JOURNEYS OF ABRAHAM

Abraham probably followed the main trade routes from Ur and Haran to Canaan, the land God had promised him and his descendants. These routes usually stayed close to rivers and settlements (above).

Abraham's father decided to leave Ur and the family headed north-west along the River Euphrates. They settled in Haran and there God spoke to Abraham. 'Leave your home and go to a land that I will show you. There your descendants will become a great nation.

Abraham and his wife, Sarah, lived in tents as they travelled south to the land of Canaan. Abraham was wealthy and they had servants and flocks of livestock. They lived a nomadic

life, camping wherever they found water and pasture and moving on again.

Abraham's nephew, Lot, travelled with them. He also had his family and servants as well as sheep, goats and cattle. The time came when there was not enough pasture land for the two of them to stay together. Quarrels broke out between the herdspeople.

Abraham decided it was time to separate. He said to Lot, 'Choose which part of the land

Abraham's journeys

Babylon

*River
Tigris*

Ur
Temple to Moon god

THE NOMADIC LIFE

*Abraham's tent would
have been made of goat's
hair cloth. A curtain
divided the tent into two
rooms: one for the men,
the other for the women
and children (below).*

you want and I'll go the opposite way.'

Lot chose the green pastures of the Jordan valley, where there was plenty of water, and headed east. Abraham settled in the hilly country near Hebron. There God spoke to him again. 'Look around you to the north, south, east and west. This is the land I promised to give you and your descendants.'

Sarah and Abraham wondered about God's promise as they grew older and had no children. But when they were quite old, God gave them a son. Abraham and Sarah loved their only son, Isaac, dearly.

When Isaac grew up, Abraham sent his most trusted servant back to Haran to choose a wife for Isaac from among his relatives. The servant brought back Rebecca, the daughter of Abraham's nephew. Isaac fell in love with her and Rebecca was welcomed into Abraham's family.

Jacob and Esau: the Shepherd and the Hunter

Genesis 25–35

Jacob rolled away the stone covering the well so Rachel could water her sheep. Wells were meeting places for village women as well as herdspeople (below).

Some years after Isaac married Rebecca, they had twin sons, Jacob and Esau. Esau loved the outdoor life and became a hunter. He was Isaac's favourite while Rebecca preferred the quieter Jacob.

When the country of Canaan suffered famine, Isaac and his family moved to Gerar in Philistia, where the land was fertile. He prospered and grew so rich that the Philistines became jealous of him. So Isaac decided that it was time to move back to the land God had promised to his father Abraham and his descendants. Isaac made a peace treaty with the king of the Philistines and he settled in Beersheba.

Years passed and Isaac grew old and blind. One day he sent Esau out hunting. 'Cook my favourite meat. When I have eaten it, I will give you my blessing before I die.'

Rebecca overheard him and plotted with Jacob to cheat Esau. Jacob pretended to be Esau and deceived his father into giving him the blessing meant for Esau. From then on, Esau planned to kill Jacob. When Rebecca found out, she urged Jacob to go and stay with his uncle Laban in Haran for a while.

On his long trek north to Haran, Jacob slept under the stars at night. One night he dreamt he saw a stairway of angels reaching to heaven and he heard God saying to him, 'I will protect and be with you wherever you go and bring you back to this land.' Next morning Jacob vowed he would come back to this spot one day and worship God. He named the place Bethel, meaning 'House of God'.

When Jacob reached Haran, he met Rachel, Laban's daughter, at a well with her father's sheep. Jacob helped her to draw water.

NAMING SPECIAL PLACES

Piles of stones were often used to mark special places, for example, the spot where an agreement was settled or, like Jacob, places where the presence of God was felt.

Jacob used a stone to mark the spot where he dreamt of the angels. He poured olive oil over it, dedicating it to God.

Sometimes, the stones were used to remind people that God was watching over them. When Jacob left Haran, he and Laban set up some stones at a place called Mizpah, meaning 'place from which to watch'.

Jacob's uncle, Laban, put him in charge of his flocks of sheep and goats. Jacob lived there for twenty years and married Laban's daughters, first Leah, then Rachel.

Although Jacob worked hard, Laban was grudging in his wages. Jacob found ways to outsmart Laban and became rich.

Eventually he knew it was time to return to his homeland. Would Esau still be angry, Jacob wondered anxiously. But Esau came from Edom to greet him and show that he had forgiven him.

Jacob and his family went to live at Bethel and God gave him the name Israel. His twelve sons were to become the heads of tribes of the nation of Israel.

JACOB'S JOURNEYS

Jacob travelled about 400 miles on foot from his home in Beersheba to his uncle's home in Haran. It was 20 years before he returned with a family, servants and herds of livestock (right).

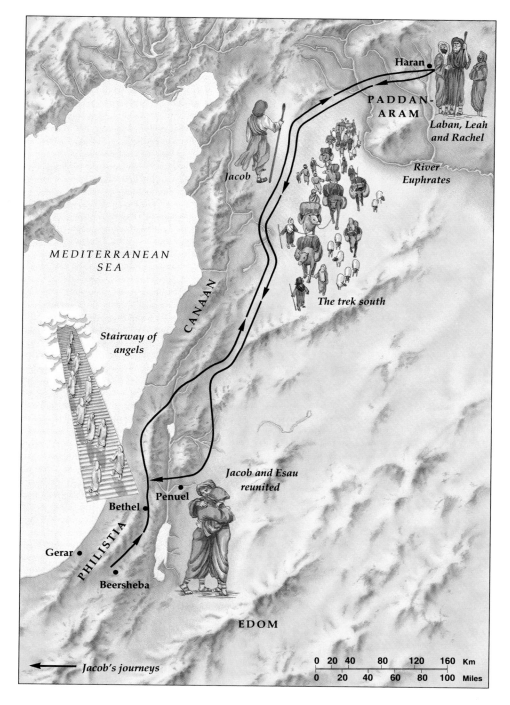

Haran

PADDAN-ARAM

Laban, Leah and Rachel

River Euphrates

Jacob

The trek south

MEDITERRANEAN SEA

CANAAN

Stairway of angels

Jacob and Esau reunited

Penuel

Bethel

Gerar

PHILISTIA

Beersheba

EDOM

0	20	40	80	120	160	Km
0	20	40	60	80	100	Miles

← Jacob's journeys

JOSEPH THE DREAMER

GENESIS 37–50

JOSEPH WAS Jacob's favourite son. His eleven brothers were jealous when his father gave him a special coat, and they hated him because he dreamt that they would bow before him. 'Do you think you are going to be king?' they jeered.

One day, Jacob sent Joseph to check on his brothers, who were looking after the sheep some way off. 'Look! Here comes the dreamer,' the brothers said. 'Let's get rid of him.' They threw Joseph into a dry well.

When some traders came by, heading for Egypt, the brothers sold him for twenty silver pieces. They killed a goat, stained Joseph's coat with blood and took it back home. Jacob mourned the son he thought was dead.

In Egypt the traders sold Joseph to Potiphar, captain of the Pharaoh's guards. Joseph was trustworthy and Potiphar made him responsible for his household. Then one day Potiphar's wife falsely accused Joseph of attacking her. Potiphar was furious and put him in prison. But God stayed with Joseph and helped him to interpret the dreams of the Pharaoh's baker and wine steward who were also in the prison. The dreams came true.

Two years later, the Pharaoh had a strange dream which no one could explain. Then his wine steward remembered Joseph. 'Bring him here,' commanded the Pharaoh.

'I cannot interpret your dream but God will tell me its meaning,' Joseph told the Pharaoh.

Joseph explained that the dream foretold seven years of good harvests followed by seven years of famine. The Pharaoh trusted Joseph and made him governor, in charge of collecting the food reserves throughout Egypt. Again, the dream came true.

When the famine reached Canaan, Jacob sent ten of his sons to Egypt to buy corn, keeping Benjamin, the youngest, at home. Joseph recognised his brothers but they did not recognise Joseph.

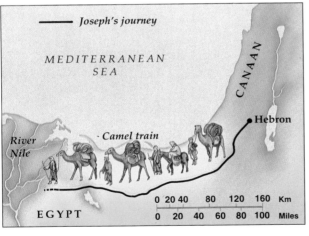

JOSEPH'S JOURNEY

Joseph's brothers sold him to traders who were heading south to Egypt with spices and resins (above).

JOSEPH'S DREAM

Joseph was 17 when he dreamt his brothers bowed to him. This came true over 20 years later when he was governor of Egypt under the Pharaoh (right).

Joseph decided to test them. 'You're spies,' he told them. 'I won't sell you any corn.' The brothers protested that they were honest men, but Joseph pretended not to believe them. He insisted that they bring Benjamin to him, and kept Simeon as a hostage. The brothers returned with Benjamin, and, eventually, Joseph told them who he was.

Jacob was overjoyed when the brothers told him that Joseph was alive, and was governor of all Egypt. 'This is all I could ask for,' he said. 'I must go and see my son before I die.'

In summer the river floods the valley

In autumn farmers plough and sow the rich mud left by the flood

In winter the crops start to grow

In spring the crops are gathered

FARMING IN THE NILE VALLEY

The River Nile was vital for survival in ancient Egypt. Its annual flood, which burst the banks and covered the land with rich, fertile silt, was essential for the farmers. They cut canals and ditches to carry the water to the fields. With careful management, this enabled them to make the water last until the next flood.

Moses: the Slave who became a Prince

EXODUS 1–12

JOSEPH'S FAMILY and their descendants, the Israelites, often known as Hebrews, stayed in Egypt. As their numbers grew, the Egyptians became afraid of them. A new Pharaoh forced the Hebrews to work as slaves, building the cities of Pithom and Rameses. He ordered that all Hebrew boys should be drowned in the river Nile at birth.

BRICKMAKING

Sun dried mud-bricks were used for building throughout the ancient world. Straw helped stop the bricks from cracking as they dried.

Straw stubble is collected from the fields

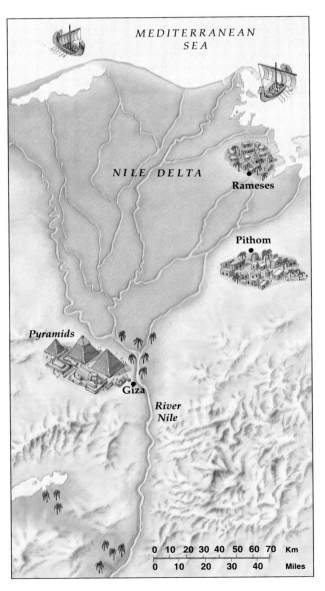

THE NILE DELTA

Every summer the Nile overflowed and left rich silt deposits on the land. Crops were harvested in spring (left).

The stubble is trampled into wet clay

The clay mixture is put into moulds to bake and harden in the sun

After several days, the hard bricks are stacked, ready for use

One Hebrew mother saved her baby by hiding him in a basket of reeds. She covered it with tar to make it watertight and placed it among the thick reeds by the river. The Pharaoh's kind-hearted daughter found the basket when she came to the river to bathe.

'Poor baby! I shall look after him,' she said. She took him to live at the Egyptian court and named him Moses.

MOSES IN THE BASKET

The thick reeds by the river Nile were a good hiding place for the basket containing the baby Moses (left).

Although Moses grew up like an Egyptian prince, he never forgot that he was a Hebrew. One day, when he was grown up, he saw an Egyptian overseer beating a Hebrew slave to make him work harder. Moses killed the Egyptian and hid his body. But the Pharaoh found out and Moses had to flee for his life to the desert, where he became a shepherd.

Many years passed and this Pharaoh died. But the Hebrews were still slaves and they prayed to God to rescue them.

One day Moses led his flock to pasture on Mount Sinai. There he saw a bush on fire, yet it was not burnt up. As he went nearer, God spoke to him. 'Moses, I am sending you back to Egypt to rescue my people.'

'How can I do that?' Moses objected. 'I am nobody. The Pharaoh won't listen to me.'

'I will be with you,' said God.

At first, the Pharaoh stubbornly refused to let the Hebrews leave, but God sent disasters on the people and their livestock, as a punishment. Finally the Pharaoh gave in and agreed that the Hebrews could go.

Four hundred and thirty years after they had first settled in Egypt, the Hebrews set off on their way back to the land of Canaan, led by Moses. It was to be a long trek with deserts to cross and battles to fight with hostile tribes, but God was with them.

FORTY YEARS TO CROSS THE DESERT

EXODUS 12–40

DRINKING WATER FOR THE ISRAELITES

There were large stretches of desert where water was scarce. At Kadesh, Moses struck a rock and water gushed out (right).

THE ISRAELITES left Egypt in a great hurry, taking their cattle and sheep with them. They would always remember the night they left and every year they celebrated the Passover meal as a reminder.

They started from Rameses and set out to cross the desert. The Egyptians, realising they had lost their slaves, followed them and the Israelites were trapped between the enemy army and the sea. But God made a dry path through the sea and they crossed safely. The Egyptian chariots stuck in the muddy sea-bed and the water rolled back and covered them.

In the desert, the Israelites missed the plentiful food of Egypt and complained to Moses. But God gave them manna, which tasted like biscuits made with honey, and flocks of quails provided meat. Finding fresh water was often difficult. At one place God told Moses to strike a rock with his stick and water came rushing out.

FOOD IN THE DESERT

Finding fresh food in the desert often presented problems for nomads and those on the Exodus. Migrating birds, such as the quail, were caught and eaten by the Israelites.

When they reached Mount Sinai, God gave Moses the Ten Commandments and other laws and instructions about worship. God promised that he would lead the Israelites safely to the land of Canaan and settle them there if they obeyed his laws.

The people moved on in stages to the edge of the Promised Land and paused to send twelve spies ahead to see the best route and the country's defences. The spies brought back samples of luscious fruit but reported that the cities were well fortified. 'We are not strong enough to attack,' said ten of the spies. Only two of them, Joshua and Caleb, spoke up bravely and said, 'God is with us. We will conquer them easily.' But the people refused to believe them and God's patience was exhausted. They spent the next forty years wandering the desert until all those who had left Egypt as adults had died. Even Moses did not live to enter the land of Canaan and it was his successor, Joshua, who led the Israelites across the River Jordan to start the conquest of the land promised to Abraham hundreds of years earlier.

No one knows for certain the exact route of the Exodus, but this is the way they probably went; southwards out of Egypt and into the large desert wilderness of Sinai, then finally on to the borders of Canaan (below).

THE LAW OF THE COVENANT

After 3 months in the desert, the Israelites reached Mount Sinai. There God gave Moses the commandments and laws by which to live.

The 10 Commandments

Worship no god but me

Do not make or worship any idols or images

Do not use my name for any evil purpose

Keep the Sabbath holy

Respect your parents

Do not murder anyone

Do not commit adultery

Do not steal

Do not tell lies

Do not long for something that belongs to someone else

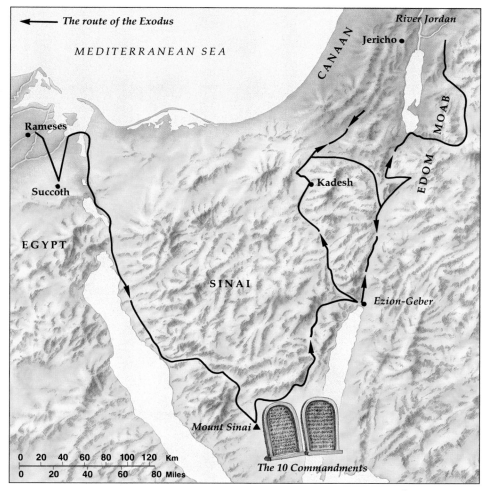

The route of the Exodus

MEDITERRANEAN SEA

River Jordan

Jericho

CANAAN

Rameses

EGYPT

Succoth

Kadesh

EDOM

MOAB

SINAI

Ezion-Geber

Mount Sinai ▲

The 10 Commandments

0 20 40 60 80 100 120 Km
0 20 40 60 80 Miles

JOSHUA THE GREAT COMMANDER

JOSHUA 6–24

To ENTER Canaan, the Israelites had first to take the stronghold of Jericho, with its high and strong walls. In the city people usually felt safe from attack. But this time they waited fearfully as it was the Israelite army who were outside. Everyone in Jericho had heard the stories of how God had made a path across the sea for them and how they had won battles against desert tribes.

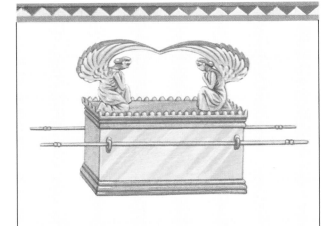

THE ARK OF THE COVENANT

The Ark of the Covenant was a box overlaid with gold. It reminded the people of God's presence with them and contained two stone slabs on which the Ten Commandments were written.

The Israelite army leader, Joshua, organised his men. 'Behind the advance guard seven priests will march, blowing trumpets. The priests carrying the Ark of the Covenant are to come next, followed by the rest of the army. You are to march round the city once in silence and come back to camp.' This went on for six days.

The people of Jericho heard only the eerie sound of the ram's horn trumpets and the tramp of feet.

On the seventh day the army marched round the city seven times. Joshua ordered, 'Shout! The Lord has given you the city.' The soldiers roared, and the city walls collapsed. The army stormed into Jericho.

News of Joshua's victory spread through the country and the Canaanite kings got together to fight for their territory.

Joshua knew the conquest of Canaan would be difficult but he knew God was on Israel's side and as long as they obeyed him, the Promised Land would be theirs.

*Joshua's campaign to
capture the Promised
Land started with
attacks on towns in the
south. Then the army
headed north and
defeated the kings of the
north (below).*

FALL OF THE CITY OF JERICHO

*When the walls of Jericho
collapsed, the Israelite
army went straight into
the city, and destroyed it
(left). The Israelites now
had a route into Canaan.*

Joshua used siege and ambush tactics as
well as open battles in his campaign. God's
instructions were to destroy the nations of
Canaan because they were evil. The
Israelites were forbidden to mix with them
or worship their gods.

Joshua defeated thirty-one kings in his
conquest of Canaan. He divided the land
among the twelve tribes of Israel, including
Philistia, which was still unconquered.

Joshua lived to be over one hundred
years old. His last advice to the Israelites
was, 'Honour God and serve him well if
you want to keep this good land he has
given you.' 'We will,' they promised.

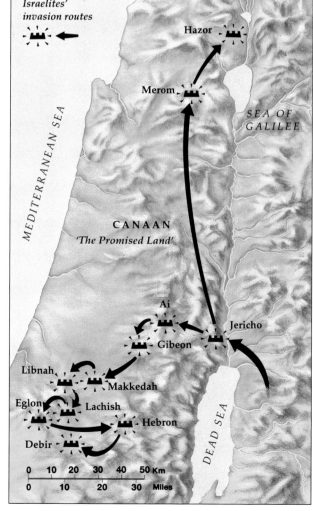

Israelites'
invasion routes

Hazor

Merom

SEA OF
GALILEE

MEDITERRANEAN SEA

CANAAN
'The Promised Land'

Ai

Gibeon

Jericho

Libnah

Makkedah

Eglon

Lachish

Hebron

Debir

DEAD SEA

| 0 | 10 | 20 | 30 | 40 | 50 Km |
| 0 | 10 | 20 | 30 | Miles |

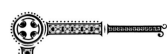

GIDEON: A MIGHTY HERO

JUDGES 6–16

AFTER JOSHUA died, the Israelites continued to fight the Canaanites. Then, as years passed, they stopped fighting and began to mix with the peoples around them. They forgot their promise to God and started to worship the Canaanite gods. God was angry with his people and allowed other nations to take them over.

One nation, the Midianites, made surprise raids from the desert and destroyed the Israelites' crops. The Israelites were helpless against these invaders on camels and asked God for help.

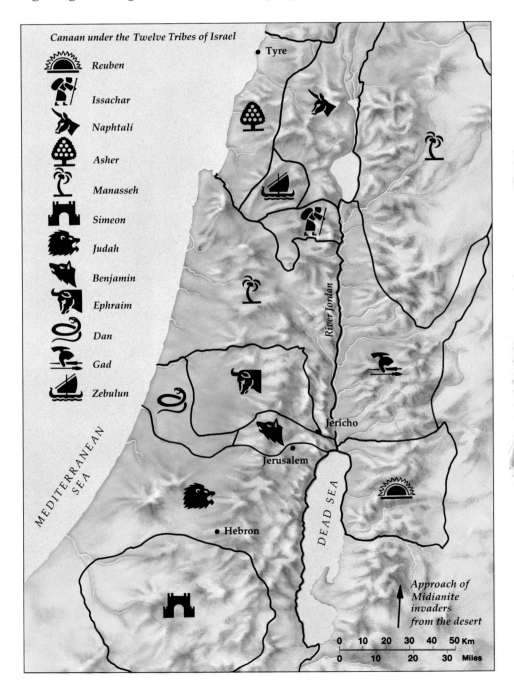

Canaan under the Twelve Tribes of Israel

Reuben
Issachar
Naphtali
Asher
Manasseh
Simeon
Judah
Benjamin
Ephraim
Dan
Gad
Zebulun

Tyre

MEDITERRANEAN SEA

River Jordan

Jericho

Jerusalem

Hebron

DEAD SEA

Approach of Midianite invaders from the desert

0 10 20 30 40 50 Km
0   10   20   30 Miles

CANAAN DIVIDED

The twelve tribes of Israel were each given land in which to settle. The symbols shown were given originally by Jacob to his twelve sons (left).

One day God sent an angel to a man called Gideon. 'God is sending you to rescue Israel from the Midianites,' he said.

'What! How can I do that?' Gideon asked. 'I'm nobody important.'

'Don't be afraid. God will help you,' the angel replied.

Gideon gathered an army and got ready for battle. But God told Gideon that the army was too big. He sent twenty thousand men home and took the remaining ten thousand to a nearby stream where he watched them drink. Most of them knelt down and lapped the water like dogs. Three hundred scooped water up in their cupped hands. 'Those are your men,' said God. 'Send the rest home.'

Gideon divided his men into three groups and gave each soldier a trumpet and a jar with a torch inside it. That night, they surrounded the Midianite army's camp. Then they blew the trumpets, broke the jars and held the flaming torches high in the air, shouting, 'A sword for the Lord and for Gideon.' The startled Midianites woke up and found that their camp was surrounded. They began to run away, attacking each other in their confusion.

Israel won a great victory against the Midianites. In the years that followed, Samson and other leaders, called judges, carried on the struggle against nations like the Philistines. These were troubled times. The book of Judges closes with the words, 'There was no king in Israel at the time. Everyone did just as he pleased'.

SURPRISE ATTACK

Gideon used the cover of darkness and a clever placing of his 300 men to confuse the Midianite army and win back the Promised Land (above).

THE GODS OF THE CANAANITES

The Canaanites worshipped a number of gods and goddesses. They believed that if they did not worship them correctly, their crops would fail. They made idols and prayed to them.

Baal – the god of fertility and weather

Bronze bull – used in the worship of Baal

RUTH AND NAOMI'S TREK

RUTH 1–4

THERE WAS famine in Israel because the crops had failed. So Naomi and Elimelech and their two sons left their home in Bethlehem and settled in Moab where there was still plenty of food.

The sons grew up and married Moabite girls, Orpah and Ruth. Then Elimelech died and, about ten years later, Naomi's sons died too. She was left alone and although her daughters-in-law were kind to her, Naomi decided to go back to her own country where she still had relatives.

It would be a long and lonely trek over ninety kilometres from the mountains of Moab along the edge of the Dead Sea and into the hilly country round Bethlehem.

Orpah and Ruth set out with Naomi to keep her company. After a while Naomi said to them, 'Thank you for coming so far with me. Now go back to your own land.'

The girls cried as she kissed them goodbye. Orpah went back to Moab but

FROM CROP TO BREAD

The sheaves of grain are piled on the threshing floor and trampled on by oxen dragging a threshing sledge. The sledge has stones or pieces of metal fixed to its underside.

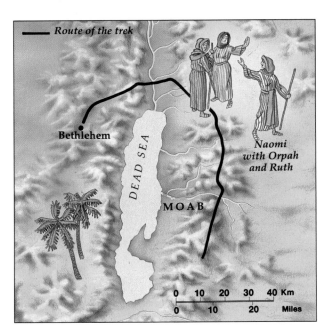

Route of the trek

Bethlehem

DEAD SEA

MOAB

Naomi with Orpah and Ruth

| 0 | 10 | 20 | 30 | 40 Km |
| 0 | | 10 | | 20 | Miles |

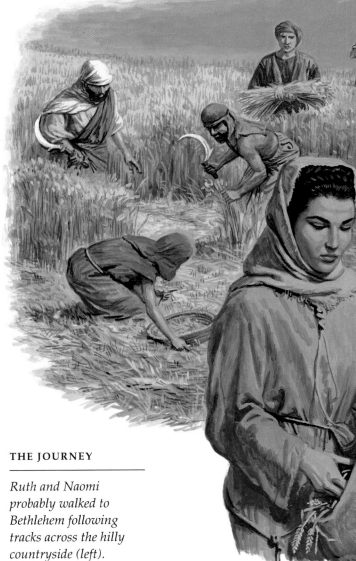

THE JOURNEY

Ruth and Naomi probably walked to Bethlehem following tracks across the hilly countryside (left).

The threshed wheat is winnowed with a fork and then sifted to remove stones.

The grain is ground, using a pestle and mortar or millstones. Water and salt are mixed in to make a dough. Flat loaves of bread are baked on a metal sheet over a fire.

THE GLEANERS

Farmers were not allowed to cut corn at the edges of their fields nor go back and pick up stray ears of corn. They were left for poor people, like Ruth, to glean or gather after harvest (left).

Ruth clung to Naomi. 'Let me go with you,' she pleaded. 'Where you live, I will live and your God will be my God.'

So the two of them continued their journey and at last reached Bethlehem, footsore and dusty. People asked, 'Is it really you, Naomi? Where's your family?'

Naomi's sad news shocked the people. They were kind to her and welcomed Ruth.

It was harvest time and Ruth went to the fields to pick up any corn left by the harvest workers, as poor people were allowed to do. A farmer called Boaz noticed her and when he found out who she was, he told his reapers to leave some extra corn for her. Ruth took about ten kilograms of grain home to Naomi that evening and ground it into flour for bread.

By the end of the harvest, Boaz had fallen in love with the girl from Moab. Naomi was delighted because he was a relative, and it was the tradition for people to marry within their tribes.

Boaz and Ruth were married. When their son, Obed, was born, Naomi loved and cared for him as though he were her own son. How glad Naomi would have been if she could have known that Obed's grandson would be David, Israel's greatest king.

SAMUEL AND SAUL: WISE AND FOOLISH LEADERS

SAMUEL 1–16

SAMUEL WAS only a young boy when he went to live in the temple at Shiloh. He helped Eli, the priest, with his duties. God used to talk to Samuel, and when Eli died the people chose Samuel to be their leader, because they respected him. At this time the Philistines were at war with Israel. They held the lands along the coast and they were fierce fighters. The Philistine warriors wore feathered head-dresses and their swords and spears were stronger and better than the Israelites' weapons.

A PHILISTINE WARRIOR

The Philistines were a fierce and warlike people. They had better weapons than the Israelites.

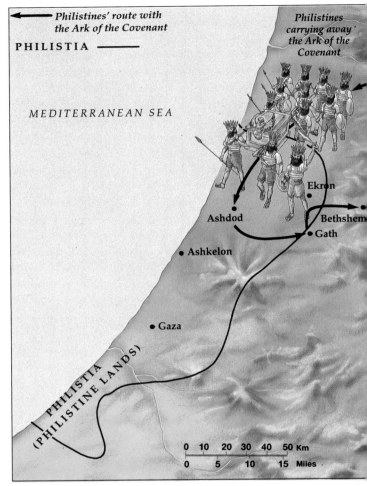

Philistines' route with the Ark of the Covenant

Philistines carrying away the Ark of the Covenant

PHILISTIA

MEDITERRANEAN SEA

Ekron
Ashdod
Bethshem
Gath
Ashkelon
Gaza
PHILISTIA (PHILISTINE LANDS)

| 0 | 10 | 20 | 30 | 40 | 50 Km |
| 0 | | 5 | 10 | | 15 Miles |

After a terrible defeat by the Philistines, the Israelites took the holy Ark of the Covenant, the symbol of God's presence, into battle, hoping they would win. But the Philistines fought even more fiercely and captured the Ark. However, disease and plague followed the Ark as the Philistines moved it from city to city and soon they sent it back to Israel.

Samuel ruled Israel wisely and when the people took his advice and returned to worshipping God, God helped them to defeat the Philistines.

When Samuel grew old, the leaders of the tribes came to see him. 'We want a king, like the other nations. Choose a king for us.'

Soon afterwards, a farmer's son, named Saul, came to see Samuel to ask his help to

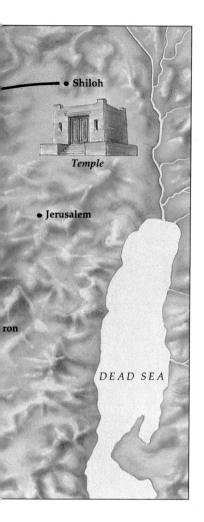

Shiloh

Temple

Jerusalem

ron

DEAD SEA

THE TERRITORY OF THE PHILISTINES

The Philistines made raids eastwards into Israelite territory to capture more land. The name Palestine comes from the word Philistia (left).

find his father's lost donkeys. 'This is the man to rule my people', God told Samuel, and Samuel anointed Saul ruler of Israel.

Saul became king of Israel and led his army to victory in his first battle. But he began to ignore Samuel's advice and disobeyed God's instructions. 'Because you have rejected God by disobeying him, he has rejected you as king,' Samuel told Saul.

Instead, God had chosen a young shepherd boy, David, to be the next king of Israel. Samuel anointed him with oil secretly. Saul did not know. Often Saul was in despair and his servants tried to comfort him, 'Let David the shepherd play his lyre for you,' and David's music soothed Saul in his black moods. Only David and Samuel knew one day David would be king of Israel.

THE ANOINTING

Saul was anointed king by Samuel in the traditional way using a sweet-smelling mixture of *olive oil and spices. Anointing was a sign of a king's appointment by God (above).*

DAVID: ISRAEL'S GREATEST KING

1 SAMUEL 17 AND 2 SAMUEL 5–24

DAVID WAS only a boy when he killed the Philistine giant, Goliath, with a stone hurled from his sling. The Philistines panicked when they saw their champion die and the Israelite army won a great victory. David was a national hero, and he became close friends with Saul's son, Jonathan. Saul was so jealous of David that he tried to kill him. Once Saul tried to persuade Jonathan to kill David, but he refused. Saul was angrier than ever, and David and a band of loyal men left the city and lived in the hills while Saul and his men hunted for them.

After Saul and his sons were killed in a battle with the Philistines, David became king. At first he ruled Israel from the town of Hebron but he needed a strong city to make his capital. One day he attacked a fortress belonging to the Jebusites. It was perched high on a rocky cliff and was well protected, but David knew there was a water tunnel under the walls. His men crawled up it and captured the fortress. David built the city of Jerusalem around the fortress and ruled his kingdom from there.

The king of Tyre sent a trade mission to David and supplied him with cedar logs, carpenters and stonemasons to build a palace.

David had the Ark of the Covenant brought to Jerusalem and the priests carried it in a splendid procession through the streets. Musicians played, the people sang and even David joined in the dancing.

David still loved to play his lyre and he wrote many songs. Many of his songs were used to lead the Israelites in worship.

David's psalms are still widely used in churches today.

DAVID'S LYRE

The instrument David played was called a kinnor. It was a lyre made of wood and sometimes decorated with ivory and silver. It was plucked with the fingers and a plectrum.

During David's forty years as king he extended his kingdom as far as the border of Egypt in the south and to the Upper Euphrates in the north. The northern part was known as Israel and the southern part as Judah. David realised that God had helped him build up his strong and prosperous kingdom. When he knew he was dying, David sent for his son Solomon. 'When you become king, be determined to do what God orders. If you do, God will keep his promise that my children will always rule Israel,' David said.

JOYFUL PROCESSION

The Ark of the Covenant arrived in Jerusalem accompanied by music and dancing. David, too, danced for joy (above).

THE KINGDOM OF DAVID

David pushed the Philistines back towards the coast and took territory from many other tribes (right).

SOLOMON'S TEMPLE

1 KINGS 3–9

SOLOMON WAS still young when he became king of Israel. One night in a dream, God asked him, 'What would you like me to give you?'

'Please give me the wisdom to rule your people,' Solomon answered.

Solomon's wisdom became famous and all kinds of people asked his advice. One day two mothers came to see him. They shared the same house and had both had babies, but one baby had died in the night. One mother claimed that the other had taken her living baby and left the dead one in its place. The other woman insisted that the living baby was hers.

King Solomon listened to them and then sent for a sword. 'Cut the living baby in two and give half to each woman,' he ordered. The real mother cried, 'Don't kill my baby! Give it to her.'

But the other woman said, 'No, go ahead. Cut it in half. That's fair.'

'The child belongs to the first woman,' Solomon declared. He knew the real mother would want her baby to live.

Under Solomon's rule, the country prospered. Soon he was able to start work on a great project – a magnificent Temple in Jerusalem where people could worship God. First he sent a request to King Hiram of Tyre who owned the forests of Lebanon. Hiram promised to supply all the timber

THE TEMPLE

The main part was 27m long, 9m wide and 13.5m high. It was built of stone with cedarwood (below).

THE GROWTH OF JERUSALEM

Solomon used forced labour to build the Temple and to extend Jerusalem beyond the city of David (right).

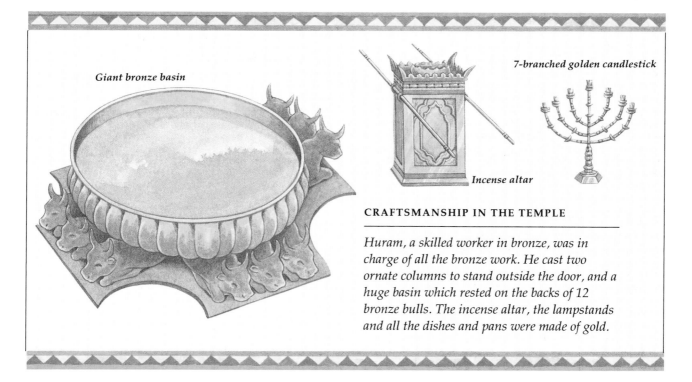

Giant bronze basin

7-branched golden candlestick

Incense altar

CRAFTSMANSHIP IN THE TEMPLE

Huram, a skilled worker in bronze, was in charge of all the bronze work. He cast two ornate columns to stand outside the door, and a huge basin which rested on the backs of 12 bronze bulls. The incense altar, the lampstands and all the dishes and pans were made of gold.

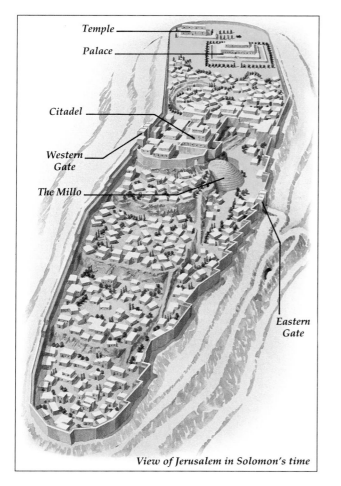

Temple
Palace
Citadel
Western Gate
The Millo
Eastern Gate

View of Jerusalem in Solomon's time

Solomon needed in return for food.

Work soon began on the Temple. The finest materials only were used. The rooms were lined with cedar panels, carved with flowers, palm trees and cherubim, and overlaid with gold. At the heart of the building was a small windowless room lined with gold, to hold the Ark of the Covenant, the symbol of God's presence on Earth.

It took seven years to complete the building. King Solomon summoned all the leaders in Israel to come to Jerusalem for the special ceremony to bring the Ark of the Covenant to the Temple.

As the priests carried the Ark into the building, sacrifices were offered to thank God. When the Ark had been placed in the inner room and the priests were leaving, a dazzling light filled the Temple.

Solomon knelt in worship and prayed, 'Lord God of Israel, watch over this temple where you have chosen to be worshipped and hear my prayers and the prayers of my people.'

CARGOES OF IVORY, GOLD AND MONKEYS

1 KINGS 10–11

KING SOLOMON took full advantage of the trade routes that ran through Israel. He became very rich because of this trade. He would buy horses in Turkey and sell them on to the Egyptians. From the Egyptians he bought chariots, which he sold to other countries.

Solomon also had a fleet of ships built at Ezion-Geber. He hired skilled Phoenician seamen to help train the less experienced Israelite sailors. They sailed to Ophir and brought back rich cargoes of gold, silver, copper, ivory, juniper wood and monkeys.

Solomon's palace was decorated with gold and his throne was the grandest at that time. It was covered in ivory and gold and had six steps leading up to it with carved lions at the end of each step and beside the two arms.

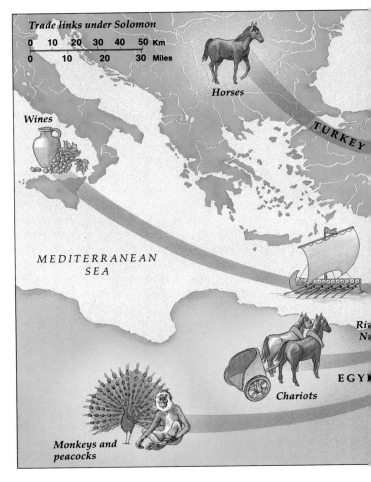

Trade links under Solomon

A PHOENICIAN GALLEY

The Phoenicians were skilful sailors, shipbuilders and sea traders. Solomon hired them for his trade in boats such as this which sailed westwards along the Mediterranean and into the Atlantic.

The fame of Solomon's wealth and wisdom spread and people travelled from far and wide to trade with him and to listen to him. Traders and merchants brought him gifts and enjoyed his generous hospitality.

The Queen of Sheba came from Arabia with many servants and a camel train laden with jewels, gold and spices to trade with Solomon. As well as trade with his country, the Queen also wanted to test his wisdom so she asked him difficult questions. Solomon answered them all and the Queen of Sheba was amazed.

He showed her round his richly decorated palace and the vast stables for his chariot and cavalry horses. She saw the huge amounts of beef, lamb, venison and fowl prepared in his kitchens and served on dishes of gold. She also visited the magnificent temple.

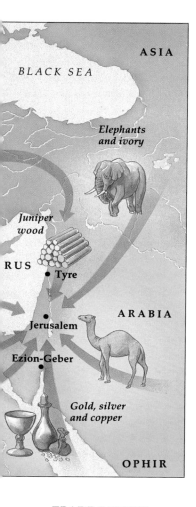

ASIA

BLACK SEA

*Elephants
and ivory*

*Juniper
wood*

RUS

● Tyre

ARABIA

Jerusalem

Ezion-Geber

*Gold, silver
and copper*

OPHIR

TRADE ROUTES

*An ancient north-south
trade route ran along
Israel's coast. Solomon
increased the nation's
trade with Egypt and
Arabia to the south, and
the Mediterranean lands
to the north (above).*

THE VISIT OF THE QUEEN OF SHEBA

*The Queen of Sheba
wanted trade with
Solomon, and to see if the
fame of his wisdom was
true. She presented many
gifts to him at his grand
palace (right.)*

Impressed, the Queen said, 'What I heard about you is true. Indeed, I didn't hear even half of it! Your wisdom and wealth are breathtaking.' She returned to Arabia, leaving Solomon a gift of all she had brought.

Solomon recognised the importance of strong trade links, and did all he could to encourage them. He married an Egyptian princess to strengthen these links with Egypt and went on to marry other foreign women, many of whom did not worship the God of Israel. Solomon loved all his wives dearly, but he let them build shrines to their own gods, and began to join his wives in their worship. God was angry with Solomon because he had broken his promise to love and obey him. God warned him that he would tear the kingdom away from Solomon's son.

DIVIDED LOYALTIES: GOD OR BAAL?

1 KINGS 12–18

KING SOLOMON had a son called Rehoboam who became the next king of Israel. Like his father, he asked for advice about how to rule but he did not ask God, as Solomon had done. Instead he consulted King Solomon's old advisers who told him to treat the people fairly and they would be loyal. He ignored their advice and listened instead to his foolish young friends who urged him to be a hard ruler.

As a result, the nation divided and only two tribes stayed loyal to Rehoboam. They became the kingdom of Judah. The remaining ten tribes formed the northern kingdom of Israel under a new king, Jeroboam.

Jeroboam did not want his people to travel to God's Temple in Jerusalem in Judah. Instead he set up two gold statues of bulls in his own territory. 'People of Israel, here are your gods,' he said. So the people of Israel disobeyed God and began to pray to these statues and to other pagan gods.

As the years passed one bad king followed another and worship of God was almost forgotten. By the time of King Ahab, the people had started worshipping the god Baal. Ahab's wife, Jezebel, believed Baal controlled the weather. God decided it was time to speak to Ahab.

One day a man called Elijah appeared at Ahab's palace with a message from God. He told Ahab that God, not Baal, was in control of the weather and there would be no more rain until God said so.

Elijah had to go into hiding because Ahab and Jezebel were so angry that they tried to kill him. During the drought that followed God protected Elijah and provided food for him. Three years later when the rivers were dry and the land parched, God said to Elijah, 'Go and tell Ahab that I will send rain.'

Elijah told Ahab to summon the priests of Baal and all the people to the slopes of Mount Carmel to test who was the real god. The priests built an altar to Baal, piled firewood on it and placed a bull on top as a sacrifice. 'Now ask Baal to send fire to burn the

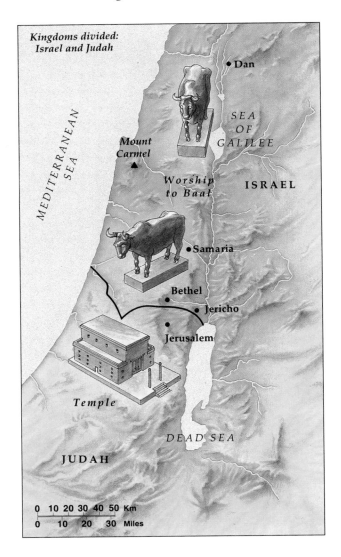

Kingdoms divided: Israel and Judah

MEDITERRANEAN SEA

Dan

SEA OF GALILEE

Mount Carmel

Worship to Baal

ISRAEL

Samaria

Bethel

Jericho

Jerusalem

Temple

DEAD SEA

JUDAH

0 10 20 30 40 50 Km
0 10 20 30 Miles

DIVIDED KINGDOM

Samaria became the capital of the northern kingdom, Israel. The temple in Jerusalem belonged to Judah (left).

CONTEST ON MOUNT CARMEL

Elijah called to God, and fire burnt his sacrifice and also the altar. The priests, people and King Ahab (in his chariot) who worshipped Baal were frightened by this dramatic challenge to their god (below).

MAKING A SACRIFICE

The Israelites had strict laws about sacrifices. The basic idea was that the sin of the person was placed on the animal which was then killed. But Canaanite religion involved sacrifices of children.

sacrifice,' Elijah challenged. All day the priests prayed to Baal and nothing happened. Then Elijah built his altar and even poured water on the firewood. 'O Lord, prove now that you are the God of Israel,' he prayed. At once flames spurted around the sacrifice. The people fell to the ground exclaiming, 'The Lord alone is God!'

Jonah, the Reluctant Prophet

JONAH 1–4

ELIJAH WAS just one of many prophets sent by God to speak to his people. The prophets not only foretold future events but they also spoke to remind the nation and its leaders of how God had helped them in the past.

ASSYRIAN LION HUNT

The King of Assyria hunted lions with his servants, firing arrows from his chariot. This drawing is based on a carving originally from the royal palace at Nineveh, the capital of the Assyrian empire.

They encouraged the people to live as God wanted them to and warned them of God's displeasure when they disobeyed him. Prophets who spoke God's word fearlessly were not always popular and it was not an easy or safe life.

God spoke one day to a prophet named Jonah. 'Go to Nineveh,' he told him, 'and warn the people about their wickedness.'

Nineveh was the capital city of Assyria, Israel's enemy. Jonah's response was to head in the opposite direction. He went to the port of Joppa and boarded a ship bound for Spain.

Jonah's efforts to run away were thwarted when God sent a violent storm and the ship was in danger of breaking up. The crew threw the cargo overboard to lighten the ship. The captain discovered Jonah asleep in the hold and woke him, urging him to pray for help. Jonah admitted that he was the cause of the storm because he was running away from God. 'Throw me overboard and it will become calm,' he said. The sailors were reluctant to do this but as the storm grew worse, they did as Jonah said. Jonah disappeared into the raging waters, the sea grew calm and the awestruck sailors vowed to follow God. Jonah did not drown but was swallowed alive by a huge fish sent by God. From inside the fish Jonah prayed to God. Three days later the fish ejected Jonah from its mouth onto a beach. This time when God said 'Go to Nineveh,' Jonah went!

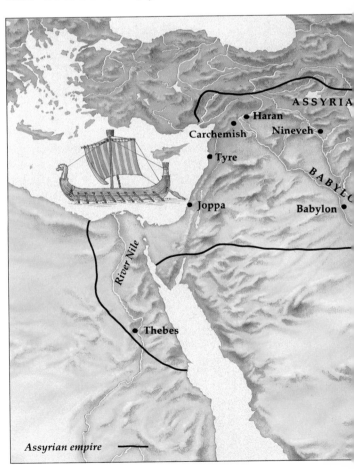

Assyrian empire ——

OVERBOARD!

Sailors threw the prophet Jonah into the stormy sea as he had asked them to do, because Jonah believed God was angry with him and this act would save the ship (above).

ASSYRIAN EMPIRE

The Assyrians pushed their borders south into Egypt, west into the Mediterranean, north into Asia Minor and east into the Persian Gulf (left).

The people of Nineveh listened to Jonah and believed that God would destroy their city if they did not change. From the king of Assyria downwards they declared their intention to give up their evil and violent ways. God relented and did not punish them.

But instead of being pleased, Jonah was angry because he did not care for these Assyrians and God had shown mercy to them.

Jonah still had to learn that God's forgiveness was offered to all and not just to his own people.

War and Exile

2 KINGS 17, 18 AND 25

A T THE time when Israel and Judah became two separate kingdoms, the powerful Assyrian empire was growing in the east.

The Assyrians were ruthless fighters and their cruelty in warfare made them much feared. They threatened Israel in the time of Ahab but he made an alliance with the king of Syria and halted their advance for a time. The Assyrians were still a threat to Israel, and the prophets of God warned the Israelites that if they continued to break God's laws and worship other gods, God would not save them from the Assyrians. The people ignored the warnings and continued to follow the customs of the surrounding nations, even sacrificing their children to pagan gods.

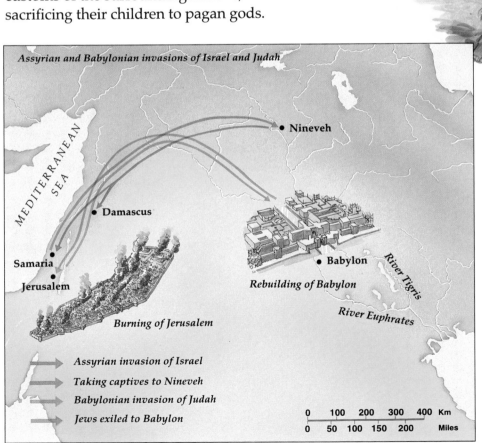

Assyrian and Babylonian invasions of Israel and Judah

MEDITERRANEAN SEA

Nineveh

Damascus

Samaria

Jerusalem

Burning of Jerusalem

Babylon

Rebuilding of Babylon

River Tigris

River Euphrates

→ *Assyrian invasion of Israel*
→ *Taking captives to Nineveh*
→ *Babylonian invasion of Judah*
→ *Jews exiled to Babylon*

| 0 | 100 | 200 | 300 | 400 | Km |
| 0 | 50 | 100 | 150 | 200 | Miles |

ASSYRIAN ATTACKS

Siege engines with ramps were made of wood and covered with animal skin. Assyrian soldiers pushed them right up to the city walls. The cover gave some protection to archers inside (above).

EXILED JEWS

The Assyrians captured Samaria, capital of Israel, in 722 BC, and exiled the Jews to all parts of their empire. The Babylonians destroyed Jerusalem in 587 BC and also took the Jews into exile (left).

In the end God allowed the Assyrians to overrun Israel and the ten tribes were taken into captivity in Assyria. They never returned to their own land.

The kingdom of Judah stayed faithful to God for a time but the people there also gave up worshipping God. Prophets like Micah and Jeremiah warned that God would abandon Judah also to their enemies. King Sennacherib of Assyria attacked the fortified cities of Judah and conquered them; but Jerusalem survived.

By the end of the seventh century BC, the Assyrian empire stretched from the River Tigris to the River Nile.

In the following century the Babylonians defeated the Assyrians. The conquering king, Nebuchadnezzar, rebuilt the city of Babylon in magnificent style. He proceeded to establish his own empire. First he defeated Egypt and then he invaded Judah. He attacked Jerusalem taking the king of Judah and ten thousand prisoners back to Babylon. Nebuchadnezzar also plundered the Temple and broke up all the gold utensils that Solomon had made. Only the poorest and unskilled people were left in Judah and a king called Zedekiah was appointed to rule them.

When Zedekiah rebelled against Babylonian rule, King Nebuchadnezzar returned with all his army and besieged Jerusalem. The siege lasted eighteen months and there was no food left in the city by the time the Babylonians breached the walls.

King Nebuchadnezzar's army burnt the Temple, the palace and all the important buildings and tore down the city walls. They carried away all the people into exile, leaving only the poorest people to work in the fields and vineyards.

Many of the exiles never saw their Judean homeland again for it was seventy years before Cyrus the Great, who defeated the Babylonians, allowed the Jews to return.

SIEGE MACHINES

The Assyrians were skilled in siege warfare. They built mounds and ramps to roll their battering rams as near to the top of Israelite city walls as possible.

DANIEL, GOD'S FAITHFUL SERVANT

DANIEL 1, 2 AND 6

THE JEWISH exiles in Babylon thought sadly of their homeland far away.

'By the waters of Babylon,
there we sat down and wept
when we remembered Zion.
On the willows there we hung up our lyres.
How shall we sing the Lord's song in
a foreign land?'

They tried to worship God, but it was not easy in a land where the people spoke a different language and had many false gods. But some were determined to stay loyal to the one true God, whatever the cost.

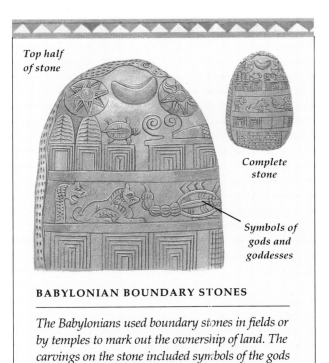

Top half
of stone

Complete
stone

Symbols of
gods and
goddesses

BABYLONIAN BOUNDARY STONES

The Babylonians used boundary stones in fields or by temples to mark out the ownership of land. The carvings on the stone included symbols of the gods and goddesses as witnesses to the land claims.

CITY OF BABYLON

Close-up of Babylon, the capital richly restored by Nebuchadnezzar. Many Jewish exiles would have passed through the main gate (below).

Ziggurat

View of Babylon

Vaulted building

Processional
way

Ishtar gate

King Nebuchadnezzar gave orders that some of the young Jewish prisoners should be trained to serve him at court. Among those chosen were Daniel and his three friends, Shadrach, Meshach and Abednego. At the start of their training they told the official in charge, 'We cannot eat Babylonian food, because our God has given us rules about the kinds of food we may eat.' The official was fearful of trouble if Daniel and his friends looked unhealthy but he soon discovered that their vegetarian diet made them fitter than the others.

Soon afterwards King Nebuchadnezzar had a dream which worried him. He sent for his magicians.'You must tell me both the dream and its meaning,' he insisted, 'or else I'll have you all put to death.'

Daniel heard the news and he and his three friends met to pray. That night God showed Daniel the dream and its meaning.

Daniel went to King Nebuchadnezzar. 'In your dream you saw a huge statue made of gold, silver, iron and clay. Suddenly a great stone fell on the statue and smashed it. Then the stone grew into a huge mountain filling the earth.' Daniel continued,' God is showing you that one day your empire will be destroyed but God will set up his own kingdom that will last for ever.'

DANIEL IN THE PIT

Thrown into a pit of lions by his Babylonian masters as punishment for praying to God, Daniel was not harmed by the lions because God protected him (above).

King Nebuchadnezzar was very impressed and made Daniel his chief adviser. Daniel thanked God and continued to worship him.

Daniel lived through the reign of King Nebuchadnezzar and his son. He was an old man when King Darius the Mede seized power. He made Daniel one of his chief officials but jealous men plotted to remove Daniel. They persuaded King Darius to make a law forbidding prayer to any God for a month. Anyone who ignored this law was to be thrown into a pit of lions. Daniel continued to pray to God as before and he was flung into the pit. But God shut the lions' mouths and Daniel's life was saved.

God still had work for his faithful servant in the land of exile.

NEHEMIAH REBUILDS JERUSALEM

NEHEMIAH 1-12

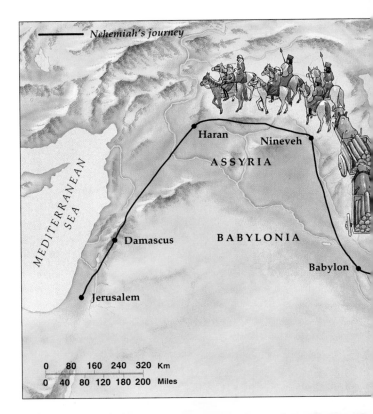

Nehemiah's journey

0 80 160 240 320 Km
0 40 80 120 180 200 Miles

THE MIGHTY Babylonian empire was conquered by the Persians, whose king generously allowed the Jews to return to their own land. Many of them left Babylon and travelled back to settle in their old towns. They started to rebuild the Temple in Jerusalem, but difficulties held up the work.

Some Jews stayed in exile. One of these was Nehemiah who was wine steward to the Persian king, Artaxerxes. One day the king asked him, 'Why are you so sad, Nehemiah?'

'Your Majesty, I have news from Jerusalem that the city is still in ruins. The people have lost heart and stopped rebuilding, 'Nehemiah replied. 'And what do you want from me?' inquired Artaxerxes.

Nehemiah prayed silently to God for help before he answered the king. He asked for permission to go back to rebuild Jerusalem and the king agreed. He also gave Nehemiah permits to travel across his empire and promised him timber for building.

When Nehemiah arrived in Jerusalem, he rode around the city at night on a donkey to see for himself what needed to be done. Next morning he met the leaders of the town and told them his plans. He encouraged them to start work and soon almost everyone in Jerusalem wanted to join in.

Nehemiah organised the rebuilding of the walls and gave people responsibility for short sections near their homes. At first all went well but some of the foreigners who had settled in the area resented the rebuilding and threatened to stop it.

Nehemiah reassured the fearful Jews. 'Remember that God is with us. He will defeat their plans.'

MISSION TO REBUILD

Nehemiah travelled about 800 miles across mountains and desert and through the province of West Euphrates to help rebuild Jerusalem (left).

WALLS REBUILT

Nehemiah and his bugler kept watch as the walls of Jerusalem were restored. Soldiers, too, stood on guard against possible attacks (below).

FESTIVAL OF SHELTERS

The Jewish priest, Ezra, encouraged people to keep old festivals forgotten by the Jews in exile. The Festival of Shelters remembered those who had first trekked across the desert to the Promised Land. Branches were made into shelters on flat-roofed homes. People sang and danced for a week.

Nehemiah placed sentries along the wall to guard it night and day. He also gave the builders weapons in case of attack. As Nehemiah walked round supervising the work, he was accompanied by a bugler ready to sound the alarm. Nehemiah's enthusiasm spurred the people and they worked eagerly and completed the walls, over a mile long, in just seven weeks. At the ceremony to dedicate the city walls to God, singers and musicians led a triumphant procession along the top of the walls.

A priest called Ezra, who had also returned from exile, helped the people to start worship in the Temple when the rebuilding was completed. Ezra gathered all the people together in a city square and read to them from the book of the law which God had given Moses. The people were upset when they realised that they had not been faithful to God. They signed an agreement that from then on, they would keep the law and not neglect going to the Temple to worship God.

LOOKING BACKWARDS AND FORWARDS

THE SMALL country of Israel was in the centre of the civilised world and was invaded and occupied by successive empires: first, the Assyrians and later the Babylonians in 586 BC.

About fifty years later, King Cyrus of Persia defeated the Babylonians and began to build the vast Persian empire. Under Persian rule the exiled Jews were allowed to return home and they began to restore their nation and also started to build local places of worship called synagogues.

The exiled Jews collected the stories of Israel's history, the laws God had given Moses and the poetry and writings of David and Solomon, and these were later included in the Hebrew Bible. Teachers of the law, called rabbis, explained the Bible.

Prophets, inspired by God, told the people how they should live their lives. Through the prophets God told the Jews that one day he would send them a special Saviour King. These stories are covered in the first part of the Bible, the Old Testament.

Hundreds of years were to pass before the prophecies were fulfilled in the birth of Jesus. During that time Palestine became part of two more empires: the Greek then the Roman.

Alexander the Great was only twenty-one when he set out from Greece, in the fourth century BC, to march east with his armies and conquer the Persian empire, which included the land of Palestine.

BETWEEN THE TESTAMENTS

For the next two hundred years Greek ways of living influenced the Jews in Palestine. This period of history falls between the Old Testament and the New Testament.

After Alexander's death, rival Greek rulers fought for control of Palestine. One of these rulers, Antiochus Epiphanes, tried to wipe out the Jewish religion. The Jews rebelled and set up their own kings for a time until the Romans conquered Palestine in 63 BC. The Roman empire was the setting for the world into which Jesus was born. His story is told in the second part of the Bible, the New Testament.

THE WORLD OF THE NEW TESTAMENT

The Romans brought thousands of soldiers into Palestine to keep the Jews under control. The Jews were forced to pay heavy taxes and were expected to worship the emperor. They refused because they worshipped God alone.

The Jews longed for the coming of the Messiah, the Saviour, promised by the prophets, believing that he would be their king and set them free from hated rulers. When Jesus came, many were disappointed because he was not the type of leader they had expected. 'My kingdom is not of this world,' Jesus said.

Bible Timelines

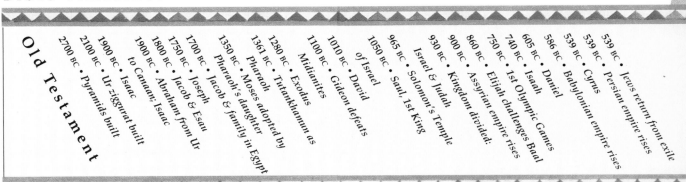

Old Testament

- 2700 BC • Pyramids built
- 2100 BC • Ur ziggurat built
- 1900 BC • Isaac
- 1900 BC • to Canaan: Isaac
- 1800 BC • Abraham from Ur
- 1750 BC • Jacob & Esau
- 1700 BC • Joseph
- 1350 BC • Jacob & family in Egypt
- 1361 BC • Pharaoh's daughter
- 1361 BC • Pharaoh
- 1280 BC • Moses adopted by
- 1280 BC • Tutankhamun as
- 1100 BC • Exodus
- 1100 BC • Midianites
- 1010 BC • Gideon defeats
- 1050 BC • David
- 1050 BC • of Israel
- 965 BC • Saul, 1st King
- 930 BC • Solomon's Temple
- 930 BC • Israel & Judah
- 900 BC • Kingdom divided:
- 860 BC • Assyrian empire rises
- 750 BC • Elijah challenges Baal
- 740 BC • 1st Olympic Games
- 605 BC • Isaiah
- 586 BC • Daniel
- 539 BC • Babylonian empire rises
- 539 BC • Cyrus
- 539 BC • Persian empire rises
- 539 BC • Jesus return from exile

After Jesus had died and risen to life, his followers went everywhere telling people that he was the Saviour and that through his death their sins would be forgiven and their lives changed. They spread the gospel.

Christianity was seen as a new religion, so the Romans imprisoned Christians and many were put to death for refusing to worship the emperor. It was almost three hundred years before Christianity became an accepted religion under the emperor, Constantine.

ALEXANDER'S INVASIONS

Alexander the Great's 12-year campaign from 334-323 BC destroyed the Persian empire that had started over 200 years earlier in 539 BC. Alexander pushed his empire as far east as the borders of India. The port of Alexandria in Egypt was built in his honour. He died in Babylon at the young age of 33 (below).

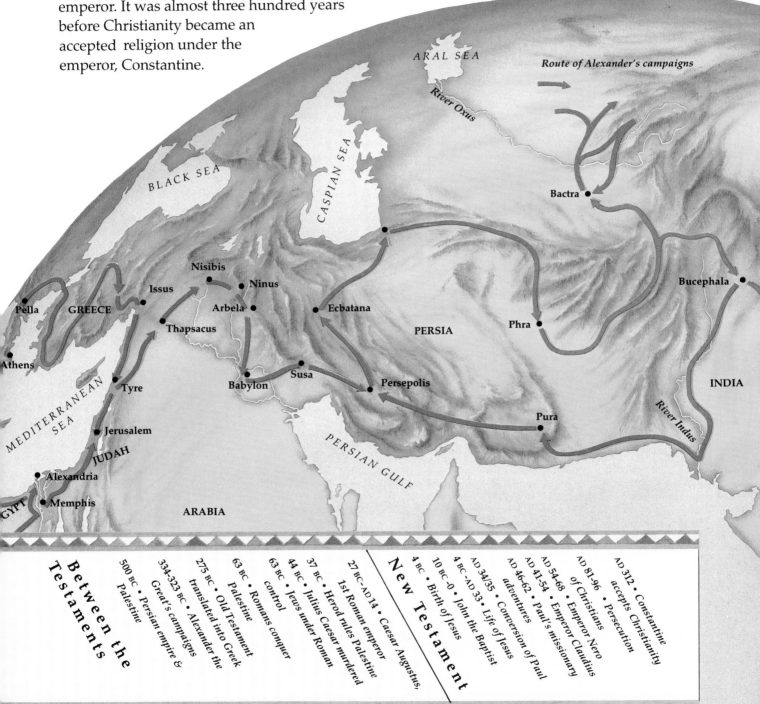

Route of Alexander's campaigns

ARAL SEA

River Oxus

BLACK SEA

CASPIAN SEA

Bactra

Bucephala

Nisibis

Issus

Ninus

Arbela

Ecbatana

PERSIA

Phra

INDIA

Pella

GREECE

Thapsacus

Athens

Susa

Babylon

Persepolis

Pura

River Indus

MEDITERRANEAN SEA

Tyre

Jerusalem

JUDAH

PERSIAN GULF

Alexandria

Memphis

EGYPT

ARABIA

Between the Testaments

500 BC • Persian empire & Palestine

334-323 BC • Alexander the Great's campaigns & Palestine

275 BC • Old Testament translated into Greek

63 BC • Romans conquer Palestine

63 BC • Jews under Roman control

44 BC • Julius Caesar murdered

37 BC • Herod rules Palestine

27 BC-AD 14 • Caesar Augustus, 1st Roman emperor

New Testament

4 BC • Birth of Jesus

10 BC-0 • John the Baptist

4 BC-AD 33 • Life of Jesus

AD 34/35 • Conversion of Paul

AD 46-62 • Paul's missionary adventures

AD 41-54 • Emperor Claudius

AD 54-68 • Emperor Nero

AD 81-96 • Persecution of Christians

AD 312 • Constantine accepts Christianity

River Nile

RED SEA

INDIAN OCEAN

THE SAVIOUR BORN IN A STABLE

MATTHEW 2, LUKE 2

THE ROMANS were the new masters of the world. Their armies marched west across Europe and invaded Britain under Julius Caesar. One of his generals, Pompey, conquered Palestine in 63 BC and brought the country into the Roman empire. The Romans kept the local king, Herod, in power as their friend and ally.

During Herod's reign, Jesus was born. While his mother, Mary, was expecting him, she had to travel with her husband, Joseph, from Nazareth in the north of Israel to Bethlehem in the south as part of a Roman check on population numbers to see who should pay taxes. Everyone had to go to his home town and Joseph's family came from Bethlehem.

When Joseph and Mary arrived in Bethlehem, they found the town packed with people who had come to register. The inn was full and they had to spend the night in the stable. There, Jesus was born, and Mary wrapped the baby in the customary strips of cloth, and laid him to sleep in the manger among the hay.

Jewish shekel

Roman denarius

ROMAN AND JEWISH COINS

Only Roman coins were allowed for paying taxes, and the Jews hated paying taxes to the Romans. Jewish coins called shekels, with images such as the 7-branched candlestick, were not accepted.

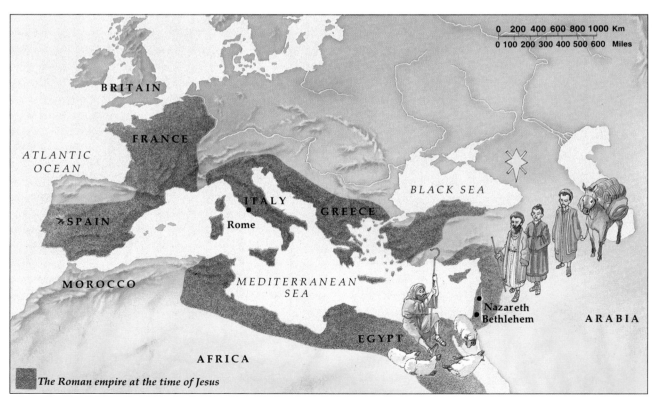

The Roman empire at the time of Jesus

THE ROMAN EMPIRE

The Romans ruled a vast empire, stretching from Britain to Egypt, and from Morocco to the Black Sea (left).

LYING IN A MANGER

After the shepherds visited Jesus, they told everyone the amazing story about the angels and the baby (above).

That night, shepherds guarding their flocks in the fields outside Bethlehem were startled by the appearance of an angel announcing, 'Good news! Today a Saviour has been born to you – Christ the Lord!' Hundreds of angels joined him, singing 'Glory to God in the highest, and peace on earth to those with whom he is pleased'.

The angel told the shepherds to look in the stable and they rushed to the town and found Mary and Joseph and the baby, just as the angel had said.

Some time later, wise men arrived from the east at King Herod's palace in Jerusalem and asked, 'Where is the baby born to be king of the Jews? We saw his star in the east and have come to worship him.'

Herod was furious and jealous. He was the king and he didn't want a rival. He spoke to the Jewish teachers. 'The prophets have said that the Messiah will be born in Bethlehem,' they told him. Herod sent the wise men to Bethlehem and told them to report back to him. He pretended that he wanted to go and worship the new king too.

The wise men found the baby Jesus and gave him rich gifts of gold, frankincense and myrrh, but they did not go back to Herod because God warned them not to in a dream.

Herod was furious at being outwitted and gave orders that all the baby boys in the Bethlehem area should be killed.

An angel appeared to Joseph in a dream and warned him about Herod's wicked plan. Joseph decided to take Mary and the baby Jesus to Egypt where they stayed until Herod died. Then they returned to Nazareth where Jesus grew up, helping his father Joseph in the carpenter's shop.

JOHN THE BAPTIST PREPARES FOR JESUS

LUKE 1,3; MARK 6

DURING THE reign of King Herod, there was a priest named Zechariah who worked in the Temple in Jerusalem. One day, as he stood at the altar, the angel Gabriel appeared and told him that his wife, Elizabeth, would have a son. Zechariah could not believe it, because both he and his wife were old.

Because of Zechariah's disbelief, the angel said he would not be able to speak until the baby was born. Gabriel also said that the baby should be named John and that he would grow up to be a great man of God who would prepare the way for the Lord.

When a baby boy was born to Elizabeth, everyone wanted to name him after his father. Zechariah shook his head and wrote on a writing tablet: 'His name is John'.

Suddenly Zechariah could speak again. The neighbours were alarmed at these events and word got around that John was a special child.

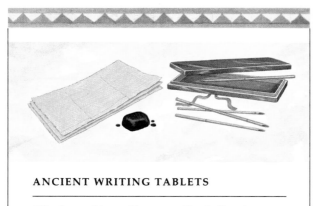

ANCIENT WRITING TABLETS

Wooden writing tablets were like shallow boxes with wax in the bottom and were written on with a stylus. The writing could be smoothed over and the tablet used again. They were common in Roman schools.

When he grew up, John lived alone in the desert. He wore a tunic of camel's hair cloth and ate locusts and wild honey. God spoke to him and sent him to preach by the River Jordan. He urged people to turn away from their sins and he baptised them in the river as a sign that they had been forgiven.

Crowds came to hear John and be baptised. People wondered if he was the Messiah but John said that he was preparing the way for someone greater. 'I am not good enough even to untie his sandals,' he said. 'He will baptise you with the Holy Spirit.'

One day, Jesus arrived at the River Jordan and was baptised by John. As Jesus came up out of the water, the Holy Spirit came in the form of a dove and landed on him. A voice spoke from heaven. 'You are my own dear Son. I am pleased with you.'

John preached in the Jordan Valley and baptised Jesus in the River Jordan, at Bethabara (below).

THE LAND OF JORDAN

The River Jordan winds through wheatfields overlooked by steep barren hillsides. Nazareth is in open hill country (right).

The lands where Jesus grew up

0   10   20   30 Km
0   5   10   15   Miles

SEA OF GALILEE

Nazareth

JORDAN RIVER VALLEY

John preaching to the crowds

River Jordan

Wilderness of Judea

Jericho

Bethabara

AMMON

Jerusalem

Fortress

JUDAH

Machaerus

DEAD SEA

MOAB

John preached to everyone and was not even afraid to tell King Herod that he had done wrong in marrying Herodias, his brother's wife. Herod responded by imprisoning John in the gloomy fortress of Machaerus. Herodias wanted John killed, but Herod did not harm him because he was afraid of offending the Jews who considered John to be a prophet.

On Herod's birthday, the daughter of Herodias danced at the feast. Herod was so pleased that he offered her anything she wanted. 'Ask for the head of John the Baptist,' Herodias said, seizing her chance.

The king was sorry but he would not go back on his foolish promise and John was beheaded. When Jesus heard the sad news, he went away to a lonely place by himself.

JESUS AT WORK IN GALILEE

MARK 1, 2, 6; JOHN 2

ONE DAY as Jesus was walking along the shore by the Sea of Galilee, he saw two brothers, Simon and Andrew, catching fish with a net.

Jesus called to them, 'Come with me and I will teach you to catch men.' At once they left their fishing and went with Jesus. Further along the beach two other brothers, James and John, were in their boat getting their nets ready. Jesus called them and they came too. Some days later, Jesus called other men to follow him until he had a group of twelve friends. These men, known as his disciples, travelled around with Jesus, helped him in his ministry and listened to his teaching. Two of the disciples, Matthew and John, later wrote their stories of Jesus' life in the New Testament gospels.

Jesus and his disciples walked the tracks to the towns and villages in the hills around Galilee, teaching people about God's love and forgiveness. Nazareth, his home town, was the only place where Jesus was not warmly welcomed.

Once Jesus was invited to a wedding in the village of Cana. In those days, wedding celebrations lasted for several days. During the feasting the wine ran out. Jesus amazed everyone by changing 600 litres of water into wine and the feast went on.

Simon and Andrew came from Capernaum on the Sea of Galilee's north shore. Jesus visited their home one day and was told that Simon's mother-in-law was in bed with fever. Jesus cured the fever. Word got around and soon the street outside was full of sick people asking Jesus to heal them.

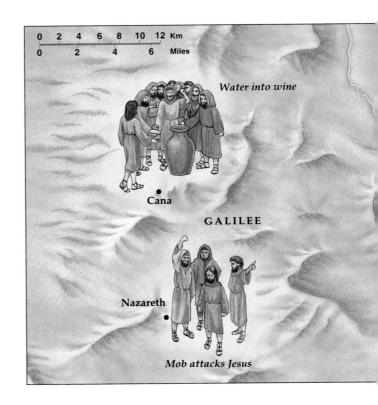

JESUS' MIRACLES

Jesus was brought up in Nazareth, home of Joseph and Mary, and it was from there, by the Sea of Galilee, that he began his ministry (above).

HOUSES IN THE TIME OF JESUS

Small with few windows, most houses had only one floor but there was an outside staircase to the roof which became an extra room.

Outside staircase

Flat roof of brushwood overlaid with clay

Animals sheltered in lower area

A few days later Jesus was teaching in another house when four men arrived, carrying their paralysed friend. They could not get near Jesus for the crowds of people, but they carried the man up the outside staircase onto the flat roof. They made a

CALL TO THE DISCIPLES

Jesus summoned James and John to travel with him and be his helpers. Simon and Andrew had already joined him as disciples (left).

hole in the roof and lowered him down into the room where Jesus was, so that he could heal him.

Soon there were so many people wanting to see Jesus that he began to teach outside by the Sea of Galilee. Jesus would sit in a boat in the shallow water while the people crowded around the water's edge. He told them stories to explain his teaching and the people loved to listen to him.

One day Jesus and his disciples set off for a quiet place near Bethsaida for a rest. But still crowds followed them and Jesus did not have the heart to send them away. He talked on into the evening until his disciples pointed out that everyone was hungry. A boy offered them five small loaves and two fish. Jesus thanked God for the food and the disciples began to hand it out. And there was plenty for all that crowd of five thousand people!

Through miracles like these, many people understood that Jesus was someone very special.

A WARM WELCOME AT JERUSALEM

LUKE 6, 10, 19

THE TIME came for Jesus to leave Galilee and head south to Jerusalem, the capital city.

Wherever he went, his disciples came too and Jesus was always teaching them about God so that they, in turn, could spread the good news to others.

There were also other teachers who did not like Jesus or his teachings. They often asked him difficult questions to try and catch him out. One day a lawyer said to Jesus, 'God says I should love my neighbour as myself, but who is my neighbour?' Jesus answered him by telling a story about a traveller who set out from Jerusalem down the lonely road to Jericho. Robbers attacked him and beat him up. As the injured man lay by the roadside, two men from the Temple came along but they ignored him. It was a Samaritan, looked down on as a foreigner, who stopped to help the poor man and took him to an inn.

The next day the Samaritan gave the innkeeper two silver coins. 'Take care of him and if you spend more I will pay you when I come back.'

'Which of the three behaved like a neighbour?' asked Jesus.

'The one who was kind,' the lawyer answered.

Jesus replied 'You go, then, and do the same'.

The stories which Jesus told always had a lesson for his listeners. Jesus said that

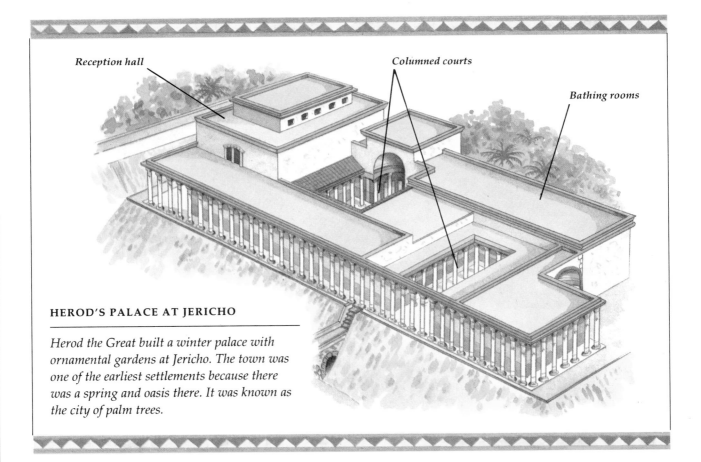

Reception hall

Columned courts

Bathing rooms

HEROD'S PALACE AT JERICHO

Herod the Great built a winter palace with ornamental gardens at Jericho. The town was one of the earliest settlements because there was a spring and oasis there. It was known as the city of palm trees.

Crowds of people were also heading for the city for the Passover Festival and they spread cloaks and branches of palm trees on the ground for the donkey to walk on. 'The king is coming!' they shouted as they welcomed Jesus to Jerusalem.

JESUS ENTERS JERUSALEM

Jesus rode a donkey into Jerusalem and was greeted by a cheering crowd (left).

JESUS TRAVELS SOUTH

Jesus headed south to Jericho, Jerusalem the capital of Judea, and Bethany, a village nearby where he stayed with friends (below).

those who heard his teaching and obeyed it were like a wise builder, who built his house on rock. When storms and floods came, the house stood firm. Those who ignored his teaching were like a foolish builder who built on sand. His house fell down in the storm.

Near Jerusalem Jesus and his disciples stopped at the village of Bethany. Jesus' friends, Mary, Martha and their brother, Lazarus, lived there. Martha quickly welcomed Jesus and his disciples and then rushed off to prepare a meal for them. Her sister, Mary, sat down and listened attentively to Jesus' teaching. Martha was annoyed at having to do all the work and asked Jesus to tell Mary to help her. But Jesus told Martha that she was too anxious over things that were less important. Mary had chosen wisely.

As Jesus and his disciples came near Jerusalem, a donkey was brought so that Jesus could ride into the city.

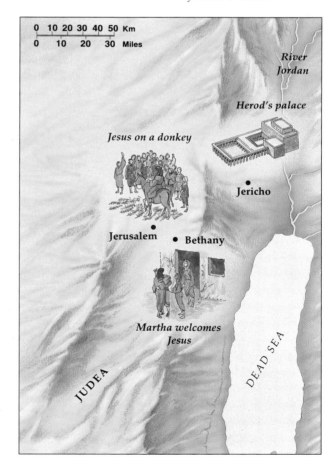

River Jordan

Herod's palace

Jesus on a donkey

Jericho

Jerusalem • Bethany

Martha welcomes Jesus

JUDEA

DEAD SEA

TREACHERY IN JERUSALEM

MATTHEW 26 & 27

JERUSALEM WAS crowded for the Passover Feast. Jesus and his twelve disciples met secretly to share the Passover meal.

'This is the last meal I will share with you,' Jesus said. He broke the bread in pieces and passed it around the group with a cup of wine. 'This is my body, which is given for you,' he said. The disciples were puzzled and sad. Jesus and his friends later walked through the dark streets to a quiet garden called Gethsemane outside the city.

A noisy crowd, armed with swords, clubs and torches, surged through the olive trees, led by Judas, one of Jesus' disciples.

'The man I kiss is the one you want,' said Judas, the traitor, kissing Jesus. Jesus was hustled roughly out of the garden, and his

THE PASSOVER FEAST

Wine

Lamb

Salad of bitter herbs

Bread made without yeast

Each year, at Passover, the Jews celebrated their nation's hasty escape from slavery in Egypt hundreds of years earlier. The traditional meal was roast lamb with a salad of bitter herbs and flat cakes of bread without yeast.

frightened disciples ran away.

Jesus was taken to the High Priest's house where the Jewish council questioned him all night. Finally the High Priest asked Jesus, 'Are you the son of God?' 'I am,' Jesus replied. 'He is blaspheming. He deserves to die,' the council decided.

Then Jesus was taken to the Roman governor, Pilate. Pilate could find no reason to condemn him and sent him to King Herod. Herod sent him back to Pilate. 'Shall I let Jesus go?' Pilate addressed a large crowd outside. 'No! Crucify him!' they shouted back.

JESUS BETRAYED BY JUDAS

Lights flickered among the shadowy olive trees as a crowd, led by Judas, a disciple of Jesus, surrounded Jesus and took him to be tried and condemned to death (left).

So Jesus was led away to die on a cross outside the city walls. Soldiers hammered nails through his hands and feet and raised the cross with Jesus on it to crucify him.

Jesus said, 'Father, forgive them. They don't understand what they are doing.' Just before he died he said, 'It is finished!' The sky turned black and the earth shook. Jesus' friends asked Pilate for his body. They wrapped it in linen and laid it in a tomb. They rolled a heavy stone across the entrance and went home sadly.

JERUSALEM IN THE TIME OF JESUS

The city of Jerusalem has been in existence since at least 3000 BC. Herod the Great shaped the city as Jesus knew it, building temples and royal palaces. The Garden of Gethsemane, where Jesus was arrested, was just outside the city. Parts of the garden are still standing today (below).

The main buildings in Jerusalem were:

 Herod's palace

 The High Priest's house

 Temple

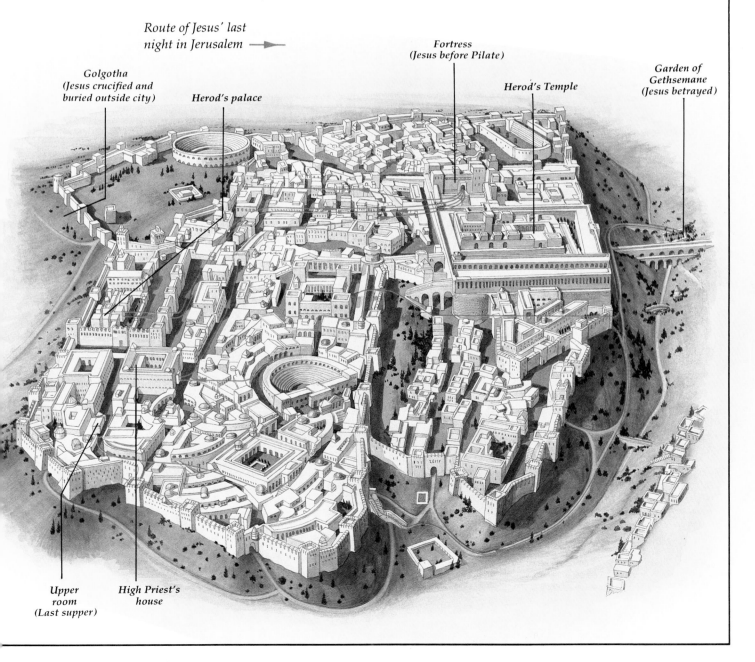

Route of Jesus' last night in Jerusalem ⟶

Golgotha
(*Jesus crucified and buried outside city*)

Herod's palace

Fortress
(*Jesus before Pilate*)

Herod's Temple

Garden of Gethsemane
(*Jesus betrayed*)

Upper room
(*Last supper*)

High Priest's house

JESUS CONQUERS DEATH

MATTHEW 28, LUKE 24, JOHN 20

THE DAY after Jesus had been buried, the Jewish leaders came to ask Pilate, the Roman governor, to put a guard on his tomb. They remembered that Jesus had said he would rise from the dead, and although they did not believe him, they thought his disciples might steal his body and claim that he had risen. Pilate agreed and the guards kept watch.

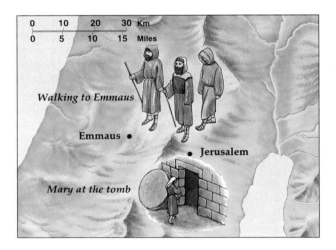

That day was the Sabbath and none of Jesus' friends went near the tomb. But next morning, as day broke, a small group of women went to the tomb with burial spices for the body.

They found that the heavy stone had been rolled away from the entrance and the body had gone. As they stood there, puzzled, angels appeared. 'He is not here. He is risen!' they told the startled women. One of the women, Mary Magdalene, wandered into the garden outside the tomb, crying in confusion. 'Why are you crying? Who are you looking for?' a man asked her.

Mary thought he was the gardener and asked him where the body of Jesus had been put. 'Mary!' he said, and as she turned to look at him, she knew that it was Jesus. She knelt in front of him and held on to his feet.

'Go and tell the others,' Jesus told her, gently. So the women hurried away, half frightened and half joyful, to tell the disciples.

The disciples did not believe them but Peter and John ran off to the tomb to see for themselves. They found that the tomb was indeed empty, the guards had disappeared, and only the burial clothes were left in the

JESUS APPEARS

Soon after his crucifixion, Jesus began to appear before some of his followers, mostly around the Jerusalem area (left).

TOMBS WITH ROLLING STONES

After the crucifixion Jesus was buried in the tomb of a rich Jew named Joseph of Arimathea. The dead bodies were normally placed on a shelf, wrapped in material with spices. The rolling stone mechanism provided a solid seal to the tomb, guarding the entrance. Rolling stones were mainly used for royal tombs, such as the family tomb of the Herods in Jerusalem.

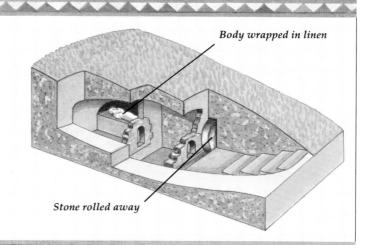

Body wrapped in linen

Stone rolled away

tomb. They went back to tell the other disciples the amazing news.

Meanwhile, the frightened guards went back to the city and told the chief priests how there had been an earthquake and an angel had suddenly appeared and rolled back the stone. They had been so terrified, they could do nothing. The priests gave the guards a large sum of money to spread the story that they had fallen asleep and that Jesus' disciples had stolen his body during the night.

Later that day, two of Jesus' followers were walking from Jerusalem to their home in Emmaus about eleven kilometres away. As they talked about Jesus and wondered who he really was, a stranger caught up with them and joined in the conversation. He told them that the prophets had foretold that the Messiah would die and rise again.

When they reached Emmaus, they invited the stranger to supper. As he took the bread and said a blessing, they suddenly recognised that it was Jesus, but immediately he disappeared. Excitedly, they rushed back to Jerusalem to tell the other disciples the good news. 'Jesus is alive! We've seen him!' they said.

IN THE GARDEN

Mary Magdalene recognised Jesus near the tomb in the garden, although at first she thought he was the gardener (above).

Good News for the World

LUKE 24, JOHN 21, ACTS 2

JESUS' DISCIPLES were eating their evening meal when suddenly they were interrupted by the two friends from Emmaus who rushed in to tell them that they had seen the risen Jesus. As they were telling their story, Jesus suddenly appeared in the room and said, 'Peace be with you'.

At first they were all terrified, thinking he was a ghost, but Jesus reassured them. 'Feel me and you will know I am not a ghost,' he said. When they saw the scars on his hands and feet from the nails that had fastened him to the cross, they began to believe the wonderful news. 'Have you any food?' Jesus asked them, so the joyful disciples shared their supper of cooked fish with him.

Jesus no longer lived with the disciples, but he appeared to them several times in Jerusalem and in Galilee.

One night Peter, James and John and some other disciples went fishing on the Sea of Galilee as they used to do before they met Jesus. They fished all night but caught nothing and at sunrise they headed for shore, tired and hungry.

They saw a man standing at the water's edge who called to them to throw their nets out on the right side of the boat. They did and miraculously the net was so full of fish they could not lift it back into the boat and had to tow it ashore.

'It's Jesus!' John said to Peter. Peter was so excited that he jumped straight into the water and waded ashore. Jesus had lit a fire on the beach.

'Bring some fish,' he said, and they ate breakfast together happily.

FISHING IN GALILEE

Fishing was a thriving industry in Galilee. There were fourteen different kinds of fish in the sea. The Galilee fishermen used both small cast nets which were thrown by hand into shallow water, and large drag nets stretched between two boats. Sudden storms often blew up on this sea, bringing danger to the fishermen.

Forty days after his resurrection, Jesus led his disciples up the Mount of Olives. There he gave them instructions to preach the good news of forgiveness of sins throughout the world, beginning at Jerusalem. But first they were to wait for the power of the Holy Spirit to come upon them. Then Jesus raised his hands in blessing and was taken up to heaven.

The disciples stayed in Jerusalem and met often to pray in the next ten days, along with other followers of Jesus.

Then on the Feast of Pentecost when all the followers gathered together to celebrate the harvest, it was as if a great gust of wind blew through the house. Something like tongues of fire spread out and touched each person.

Suddenly they were able to speak in other languages and they rushed out and began to talk about Jesus to all the Jews who had come from many countries to Jerusalem for the festival. Some people jeered at them, but many crowded round to listen and that same day three thousand people were baptised in the name of Jesus and became his followers.

The disciples' task of telling the Good News had begun. Soon there would be followers of Jesus all over the Roman Empire.

ON THE BEACH

Peter waded through the waters of Galilee on recognising Jesus by the shore (left).

JESUS GATHERS HIS DISCIPLES

Jesus appeared to his eleven disciples (Judas had killed himself) (right).

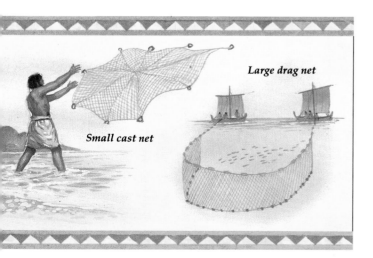

Large drag net

Small cast net

TURN-ABOUT ON THE DAMASCUS ROAD

ACTS 3, 4, 9

THE NEW followers of Jesus met in each other's homes to share meals and to hear about Jesus. They also went often to the Temple to praise God. One day as Peter and John were going into the Temple, a lame man sitting by the gate begged for money. Peter looked at him. 'I have no money but I give you what I have; in the name of Jesus get up and walk!' he ordered.

Peter reached down and helped the man to stand. At once strength came into his feet and legs and he started walking. He rushed into the Temple, leaping and jumping and praising God. A crowd quickly gathered and stared in amazement at Peter and John. Peter explained that it was the power of Jesus that had made the lame man walk. When the priests and Jewish leaders heard this, they were furious. They thought they had got rid of Jesus for good. Peter and John were arrested and put in prison.

The Jewish council warned Peter and his friends strongly to stop preaching about Jesus. Peter replied that they had to do what God wanted even if it meant disobeying the Jewish leaders.

As more and more people in Jerusalem became followers of Jesus, the Jewish authorities became more determined to stop them. A man named Saul went round the homes of believers in Jesus and dragged many off to prison. One man, Stephen, was taken out of the city and stoned to death. As a result, some of Jesus' followers fled from Jerusalem to smaller towns in Judea and took the gospel north to Samaria. When Saul realised this was happening, he set off for Damascus with letters of authority from the High Priest to arrest followers of Jesus. He had almost reached the city when suddenly a dazzling light blinded him and he fell on the ground. 'Saul, Saul, why are you attacking me?' a voice asked.

'Who are you, Lord?' the confused Saul replied.

'I am Jesus, whom you are persecuting,' the voice said. 'Get up and go into Damascus. You will be told what to do there.'

In a daze Saul got up but he still could not see. The men with him led him to the city. He ate no food and it was three days before his sight was restored.

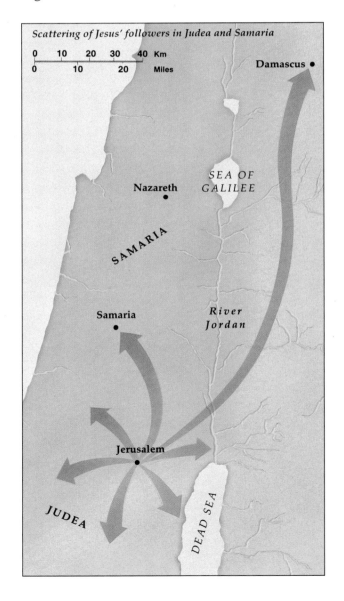

Scattering of Jesus' followers in Judea and Samaria

Saul's life was completely changed. He became a believer in Jesus and joined the others spreading the Good News. He changed his name to the Roman name, Paul, and spent the rest of his life travelling through the countries around the Mediterranean, spreading the message of Jesus.

SAUL SEES THE LIGHT

Saul was converted as a believer when a blinding vision of Christ crossed his path to Damascus, as he went to persecute believers in Jesus (above).

SPREADING THE WORD

After Stephen was stoned to death for being a believer, Jesus' followers began preaching away from Jerusalem into all parts of Judea (left).

Greek houses

MEETING PLACES TO HEAR THE WORD

Long before churches were built, the followers of Jesus met in ordinary houses. Christians in the Greek city of Corinth may have met in a house like this to listen to Paul.

PAUL'S MISSIONARY ADVENTURES

ACTS 13-28

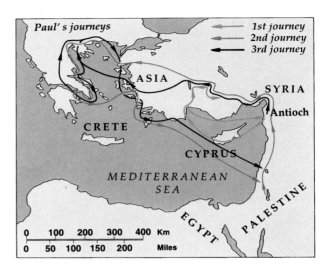

Paul's journeys

1st journey
2nd journey
3rd journey

ASIA

SYRIA

Antioch

CRETE

CYPRUS

MEDITERRANEAN SEA

EGYPT

PALESTINE

| 0 | 100 | 200 | 300 | 400 Km |
| 0 | 50 | 100 | 150 | 200 Miles |

THE ROMANS built good straight roads throughout their empire. This made it easier for Paul and others to take the gospel to the towns and cities of Asia Minor.

Paul and his friend, Barnabas, spent a year in the city of Antioch in Syria teaching a large group of followers of Jesus. It was here that the believers were first called Christians, probably as a nickname.

Paul and Barnabas then sailed to Cyprus and preached in the Jewish synagogues there. They also sailed to Asia Minor and made their way over high mountain passes into Turkey, persuading many to become Christians.

However, Paul and his companions were not always welcomed and sometimes their lives were threatened as in Lystra and in Philippi where Paul was beaten and put in jail. But Paul helped groups of believers to form Christian congregations in large cities like Corinth and in many smaller towns.

PAUL'S MISSIONARY JOURNEYS

Between AD 46 and AD 57, Paul made three great journeys from Antioch, converting people to Christianity (above).

PAUL'S JOURNEY TO ROME

On the way to Rome Paul was caught in a storm that lasted two weeks. The ship was wrecked, but everyone managed to swim to shore on the island of Malta (right).

PAUL PREACHES

In Athens, Paul preached amongst the statues of the Greek gods and goddesses in the market place (right).

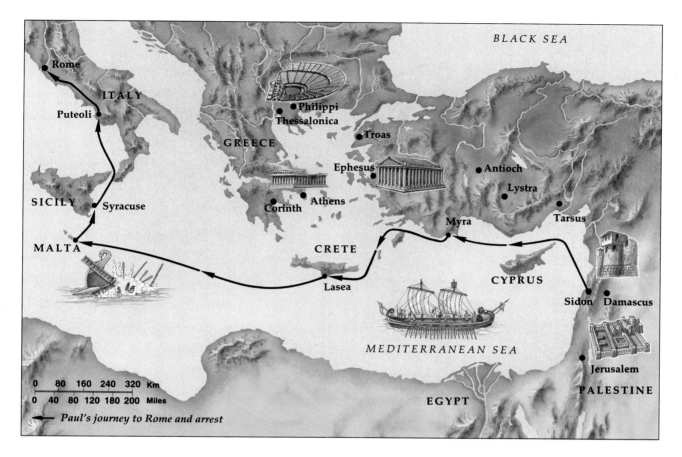

Paul revisited many groups and wrote letters to encourage the new Christians. Several of these letters can be found in the Bible. For example, the book of Ephesians is Paul's letter to the people of Ephesus.

After his third long journey, Paul returned to Jerusalem where he was arrested on a false charge and handed over to the Roman governor at Caesarea. After two years in prison Paul appealed to be sent to Rome to be tried by the emperor. On the long winter voyage to Rome, the grain ship carrying Paul and other prisoners ran into a furious storm. Paul calmed the frightened crew and though the ship was wrecked off Malta, everyone survived as Paul had said would happen.

In Rome, Paul was put under house arrest, but still encouraged people to follow the way of Jesus until his death at the order of Emperor Nero, who did his best to stamp out Christianity. He did not succeed.

PAUL'S LETTERS

Jesus' disciples wrote several letters to encourage other people to become Christians. They explained the principles of the Christian way of life to people living in different cities.

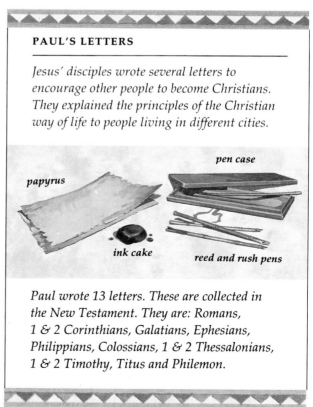

papyrus

pen case

ink cake

reed and rush pens

Paul wrote 13 letters. These are collected in the New Testament. They are: Romans, 1 & 2 Corinthians, Galatians, Ephesians, Philippians, Colossians, 1 & 2 Thessalonians, 1 & 2 Timothy, Titus and Philemon.

INDEX

Numbers in **bold** refer to maps
Numbers in *italics* refer to illustrations

Abraham 10
    journey to Canaan **10-11**
Adam and Eve 8
Ahab and Jezebel 34
Alexander the Great **45**
Ark, Noah's *8*
    of the Covenant 20, 26,
    28, 30
Assyrian empire **36-37**
    lion hunt *36*
    siege *38*

Baal *23*, 34-35
Babel, Tower of 9
Babylon *38*, **40**, 40
Babylonian boundary
    stones *40*
Baptism by John 48-49
Barnabas 62
Bethlehem 24-25, 46-47
Boaz 25
Brickmaking *16-17*

Canaan **6-7**
    conquest by Israel **21**
    geography 7
    tribal areas **22**
Canaanite gods *23*

Daniel 41
David
    his kingdom **29**
    king 28-29
    musician *28*
    shepherd 27

Eden, Garden of 8
Eli 26
Elijah 34
Esau 12-13
Exile, routes of **38**
Exodus route **19**
Ezra 43

Festival of Shelters *43*
Fishing 50, 51, 58-59
Flood 9

Gideon 22-23
Gleaners 25
Grain, threshing *24-25*

Herod 46-47
House, Greek *61*
Houses in Jesus' time *51*

Isaac 11, 12
Israel and Judah **34**
Israel today **6**

Jacob 12-13
    journey to Haran **13**
Jericho 20-21, *52*
Jerusalem 27
    at the time of Jesus *52-53, 55*
    destruction 39
    rebuilding 42-43
    Solomon's *31*
Jesus' life 48-59
Jewish coins *46*
John the Baptist 48-49
Jonah 36-37
Jordan, river **7**, *49*, **49**
Joseph 14-15
    journey to Egypt **14**
Joshua 20-21

Manna 18
Midianites 22-23
Moses 17

Naomi 24-25
Nebuchadnezzar 39, 41
Nehemiah 42-43
    journey to Jerusalem **42-43**
Nile, river **16**
    farming *15*

Nineveh 36-37
Noah 9

Passover Feast 54
Paul 62-63
    his travels **62, 63**
Pentecost Feast 59
Persians 42, 44-45
Pharaoh 14, 16, 17
Philistine territory **26**, 27
    warrior *26*
Place names 12
Promised Land **7**, 10, 18

Quail *18*
Queen of Sheba 32-33

Rebecca 11, 12
Roman empire **46**
    coins *46*
Ruth 24-25
    journey to
    Bethlehem **24**

Sacrifices *35*
Samuel 26-27
Sarah 11
Saul, king 26-27
Saul (Paul) 60-61
Solomon 30-33
    trade routes **32-33**

Temple crafts *31*
    destruction 39
    rebuilding 43
    Solomon's *30*, 31
Ten Commandments 18
Tents *11*
Tombs 57

Ur, jewellery *10*

Writing tablets *48*

THE WATTS HISTORY OF SPORTS

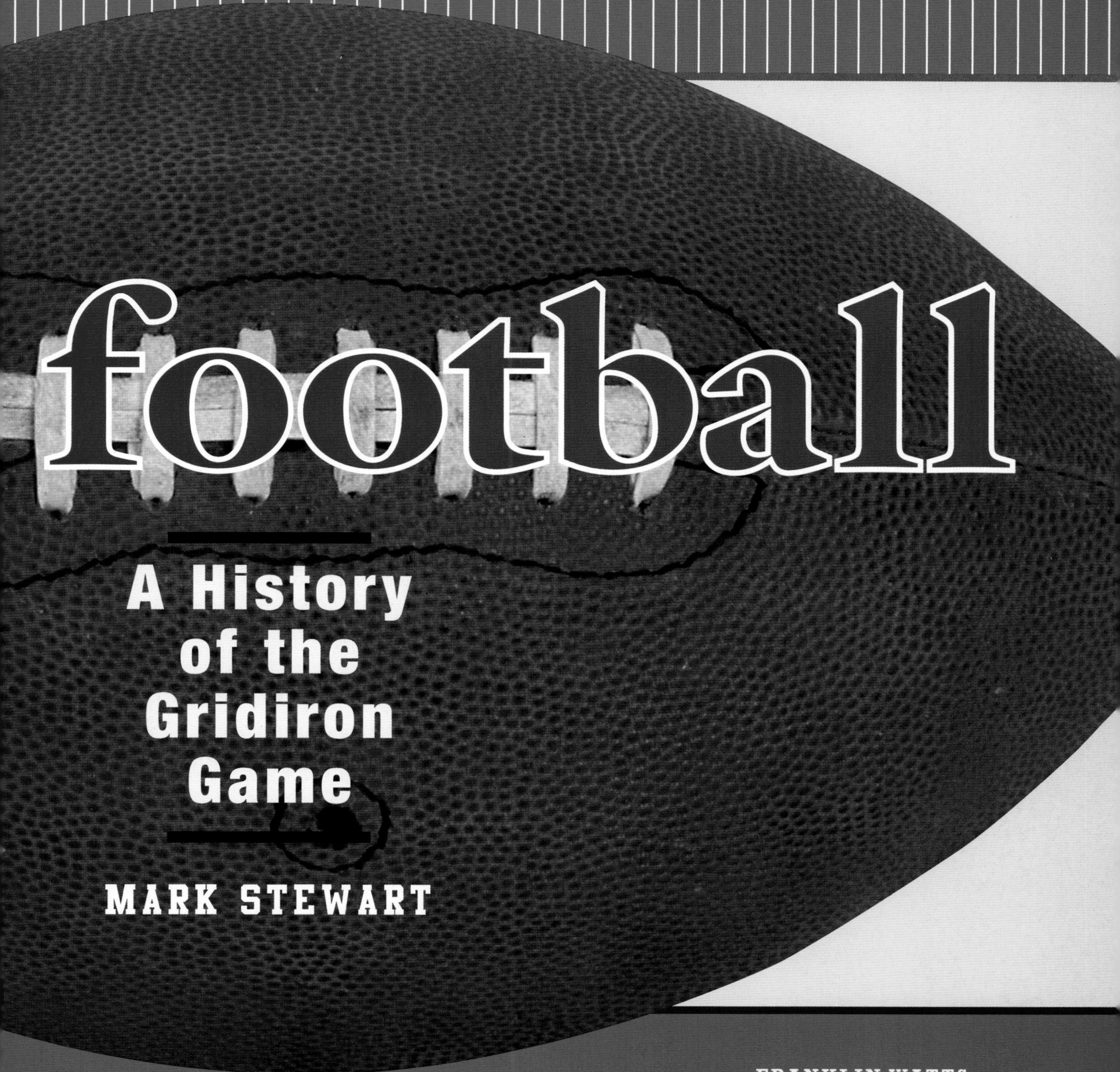

football

A History of the Gridiron Game

MARK STEWART

FRANKLIN WATTS
A Division of Scholastic Inc.
New York • Toronto • London • Sydney • Auckland
Mexico City • New Delhi • Hong Kong
Danbury, Connecticut

Cover design by Dave Klaboe   Series design by Molly Heron
Photographs ©: AllSport USA: 112 (Brian Bahr), cover inset (Mike Powell); AP/Wide World Photos: 103 (John Swart), cover inset, 35, 38, 52, 69, 82; Brown Brothers: cover inset, 19, 27, 40; Corbis-Bettmann: 16; NFL Photos: 47 (AP/Wide World Photos), 67 (Morris Berman), 64 (Vernon Biever), 78 (George Gojkovich), 98 (George Gojkovich), 105 (Paul Jasienski), 57 left (Frank Kuchirchuk), 70 (Neils Lauritzen), 59 (Darryl Norenberg), 60 (Hy Peskin), 100 (Russ Reed), 72 (Tomsic), 57 right (Herb Weitman), 97 (Lou Witt), 15, 23, 26, 34, 94 (Michael Zagaris); Reuters/Archive Photos: cover inset (Sarah Fawcett), 107 (Mike Blake), 95 (Gary Hershorn), cover inset (Adrees Latiff), 49 left (New York Times Co.), 104 (John Sommers II), 86; Sports Illustrated Picture Collection: 111 (John Biever), 75 (Time, Inc.), cover inset (Walter); SportsChrome East/West: 113 (Jeff Carlick), 80 (Brian Drake), 109 (Rich Kane), 110 (Rob Tringali Jr.), 93, 96; Team Stewart, Inc.: cover inset, 5 (Harper's Weekly), 9 (Intercollegiate Football), cover inset, 21, 25, 30, 32, 37, 42, 44, 45, 48, 51, 58, 63 right, 65, 68, 73, 84, 85, 90; UPI/Corbis-Bettmann: cover inset, cover inset, 49 right, 56, 63 left, 71.

Library of Congress Cataloging-in-Publication Data
Stewart, Mark
    Football: A history of the gridiron game / Mark Stewart.
    p. cm. — (The Watts history of sports)
    Includes bibliographical references and index.
    Summary: Discusses the origins and evolution of the game of football,
        as well as memorable events and key personalities in the game's history.
    ISBN 0-531-11493-7
    1. Football—United States—History—Juvenile literature.
    [1. Football—History.] I. Title II. Series.
    GV950.S74 1998
    796.332'0973—dc21   98-25038
                                                         CIP
                                                         AC

6 7 8 9 10 R 10 09 08   62

CONTENTS

The History of Football   **4**

A Football Timeline   **114**

Appendix A: AP National Collegiate Champions   **128**

Appendix B: Heisman Trophy Winners   **128**

Appendix C: College Statistical Records   **129**

Appendix D: National Football League Champions   **131**

Appendix E: Champions of Rival Professional Football Leagues   **133**

Appendix F: NFL Most Valuable Player Awards   **134**

Appendix G: Professional Football Statistical Records   **134**

Appendix H: Members of the Pro Football Hall of Fame   **137**

For More Information   **139**

Index   **140**

Origins

In 1823 an English schoolboy named William Webb Ellis did something that would forever change the course of sports. He was playing the popular English game of football, which at the time was primarily a kicking game, a little like today's soccer. Ellis caught a long ball (as was permitted by the rules of the day) just as a nearby bell tower began chiming five o'clock. By school rules, this signaled the end of all games. Instead of placing the ball on the ground and taking a free kick, William tucked the ball under his arm and barreled up the field past his stunned schoolmates, crossing the goal line for the winning score before the bell struck a fifth and final time. Ellis was chided for his skirting of the rules, but the more the boys at the Rugby School thought about history's first "buzzer-beater," the more they liked the idea of allowing a player to run with the ball. Soon, this sport became known as rugby—the direct ancestor of today's American football.

Rugby, like many other English sporting pastimes, found its way to the United States in the early 19th century and was adopted by young men of school age. And Americans, as they seemed to do with most sports of English origin, soon put their own special spin on the game. In 1827, on the first Monday of the school year, the freshman and sophomore classes at Harvard University chose their fastest, strongest athletes, and they had at each other in a particularly bone-rattling form of rugby that became an

The mad rush is on: players converge on the ball in this depiction of a 19th-century rugby contest.

annual tradition with a graphically descriptive name—"Bloody Monday."

Bloody Monday contests featured a round ball and had practically no rules—the field had no boundaries, except for opposing goal lines, and the number of players per side was rarely limited. Broken bones, shattered jaws, black eyes, and cracked teeth were commonplace, and play would usually disintegrate into all-out melees interrupted every so often by an actual score. Apparently the game had appeal as a violent test of manhood—during the 1840s, Bloody Monday traditions were founded at Yale, Amherst, and Brown. However, the unruliness of these contests, both on and off the field, brought about their demise; in 1858 in New Haven, Connecticut, where Yale freshman and sophomores had been squaring off each fall on the city green, the authorities decided to deny the students the use of the green. And in 1860 the Harvard faculty put an end to a sport they rightly saw as a thin excuse for outright mayhem.

The rules of rugby (or "the kicking game") became more highly defined during the 1860s, especially after the game of soccer took measures to distinguish and distance itself from its more violent cousin. With these clearer rules, American football became less like soccer, more like rugby. Soon after, it began to take its own distinctive shape, first at the secondary school level and later in several North American colleges. Boston Latin, Roxbury High, Dorchester High, Boston English, and the Dixwell School engaged in an organized (but still very rudimentary) form of football on Boston Common during the 1860s, and in 1862 the first football "club" was formed in that city. They called themselves the Oneida Football Club, and soon they were

playing other clubs in the area. The Oneidas were made up of young men interested in playing this rough and tumble game after their school days, and they went four years without allowing an opponent to cross their goal line.

Despite efforts to make it a game unique unto itself, American football as it was played in the 1860s was still part soccer, part rugby. Each school embraced its own version, and many adopted rules aimed at limiting the game's violence. Two New Jersey universities, Princeton and Rutgers (at that time called Kings College), happened to play by very similar rules. Given their proximity to each other—and the long, sometimes intense rivalry that for years had existed between their respective student bodies—it seemed only natural that they meet on the football field. Prior to this time, the strongest and most daring young men on each campus had been focusing their competitive energies on stealing and re-stealing a huge cannon over which generals Howe and Washington had struggled during the Revolutionary War. Princeton had put an end to this circle of thievery by sinking the gun in a block of concrete. Apparently football was the logical competition to replace it.

On November 6, 1869, the Princeton boys took a short train ride to New Brunswick, and the two schools engaged in the first intercollegiate football game. The rules of the game itself were typical of football at the time. The ball could only be advanced with the foot or the head. No ball-carrying was allowed, but the ball could be caught on the fly or after one bounce and be placed on the ground—a defending team might do this and quickly boot the ball other way, deep into enemy territory. The object was to kick the ball across the other team's goal line, between two posts set 25 feet apart. Records indicate that there were 25 men to a side. They wore no uniforms, although several individuals on the Rutgers side sported scarlet material wrapped tightly around their heads.

On the surface the Rutgers-Princeton game sounds more like soccer than modern football, but there was one very important wrinkle that was very much an American invention: "interference" or, as it is called today, blocking. When a Princeton player dribbled the ball upfield, soccer-style, his teammates formed a human wall in front of him, and they pushed, shoved, or otherwise displaced the Rutgers defenders. Rutgers in turn pushed and shoved right back. When the ball could no longer be advanced forward, it was kicked toward the opposing goal. If it did not go across the line, play continued the other way, with Rutgers on the offensive and Princeton attempting to stop the advance. It is important to note that blocking was a thoroughly American twist—not even the more violent sport of rugby allowed teammates to clear a path for the ball carrier.

Rutgers's smaller, quicker athletes prevailed over Princeton's bigger, slower players by a score of 6-4. No one was badly hurt, and the game included a Princeton goal scored by a Rutgers player who had lost his bearings. The crowd got into the game, both figuratively and literally. Princeton rooters who had accompanied the team uttered what is believed to be the first college cheer—a chant that had first been heard as New York's fabled Seventh Regiment passed through Princeton on its way south in the early days of the Civil War. And among the 200-plus spectators were several perched upon a wooden fence, which gave

way when several players smashed into it in pursuit of the ball. Two weeks later, the schools played a return match in Princeton, which the home team won 8-0. The game had to be stopped numerous times because the ball kept deflating. The players took turns blowing it back up.

One year later, Columbia University played its first game of intercollegiate football, losing to Rutgers 6-3. Yale and Cornell also began to play football, with each class (freshman through senior) fielding its own squad. Harvard rediscovered football, too, but its game was less like soccer and more like the old Bloody Monday, only with a few more rules. Kicking was still a big part of the game, but a player could scoop up the round ball and run with it if he was so inclined. In Harvard's version of football, stopping a ball carrier was accomplished by restraining him or knocking him down, and thus "tackling" in the modern sense became part of the game.

Since no other American colleges were playing this rough variation of the game, Harvard formed a football association of its own. It organized and governed games between the various classes at the university. Harvard was the country's leading school at this time, in everything from education to sports. So when the other football-playing universities convened in New York in 1873 to form the first intercollegiate football association, they encouraged Harvard to join them. Harvard declined, citing the fundamental differences in the rules of its brand of football.

Early in 1874, the rugby team of McGill University in Montreal, Canada, challenged Harvard's football association to a series of games. Harvard accepted, and the two captains began working out the details. McGill's David Roger suggested that two games be played in Cambridge that spring. The first would be played under Harvard's rules, and the second under McGill's, which played the more evolved form of rugby just beginning to cross from England over to Canada, and used an egg-shaped rugby ball. Harvard captain Henry Granted agreed, although it is doubtful that anyone on his squad had ever seen rugby played, or had even seen the odd-shaped ball. The first game went to Harvard, 3-0. The second (which is presumed to be the first intercollegiate rugby game played in the United States) ended in a scoreless tie.

The Harvard men were impressed. As much as they liked their rough-and-tumble version of football, the Canadian game was much more exciting. They liked the hard tackling and quick lateral passes. They were intrigued by the ball, which bounced erratically compared to theirs. And they particularly liked one Canadian modification to British rugby rules: when a ball carrier plowed through his opponents and crossed the goal line, his team was awarded something called a "touchdown." They struggled to understand the offsides and out-of-bounds rules, and marveled at the drop-kick, which the Canadians could execute from a stationary start or on the dead run.

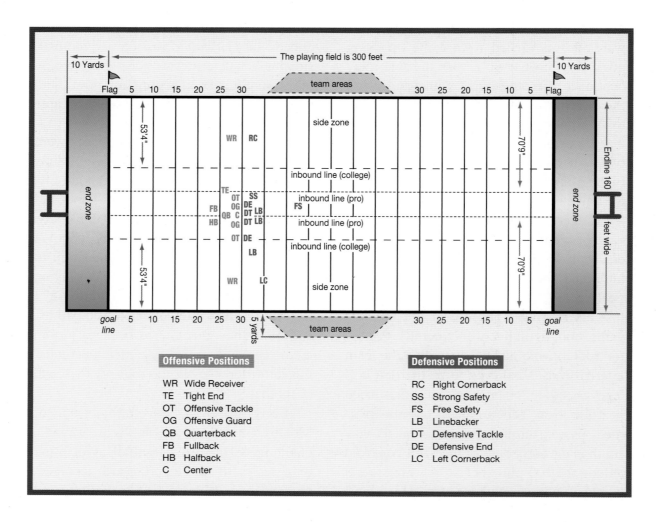

Offensive Positions

WR	Wide Receiver
TE	Tight End
OT	Offensive Tackle
OG	Offensive Guard
QB	Quarterback
FB	Fullback
HB	Halfback
C	Center

Defensive Positions

RC	Right Cornerback
SS	Strong Safety
FS	Free Safety
LB	Linebacker
DT	Defensive Tackle
DE	Defensive End
LC	Left Cornerback

The Harvard men practiced during the summer and traveled to Montreal that fall, and there they beat McGill at its own game by a score of 3-0. At the time, touchdowns (like kicked goals) were counted as only one point.

The following year, Harvard turned its attention to its traditional athletic rival, Yale. The 1875 team captain, Nathaniel Curtis, challenged William Arnold, his Yale counterpart, to a game that fall. Two thousand spectators paid 50 cents each to see the game, which was held in New Haven on November 13, 1875. Both teams wore uniforms—a first for college football—and Harvard won 4-0. Although overwhelmed and often confused, the Yale players found the game very much to their liking. And so one of the greatest rivalries in all of sports began. In the immense crowd that day were two of Princeton's top soccer players. They too were captivated by the game they saw, and upon their return to New Jersey they set about convincing their teammates that they should switch to this new kind of football. It took a year, but they were successful, and in the winter of 1876 invitations to meet and form an Intercollegiate Football Association were sent by Princeton to Harvard, Yale, and Columbia.

Delegates from the four universities met in Springfield, Massachusetts. The schools had been playing football for at least a year by this time, but each had added its own subtle touches to the standard Rugby Union Code established in England in 1872. The delegates agreed that everyone had to play by the same rules, but not necessarily by English rules. For instance, touchdowns were allowed, but accorded just one point. Goals kicked from the field—considered much more difficult—were worth four. A

Walter Camp, often called "the father of college football." He was the driving force behind the development of football's rules and regulations.

neutral referee and two "judges"—one from each side—would officiate games, and there would be two 45-minute halves. The field was standardized at 140 yards long and 70 wide, and teams were set at 15 men per side (the standard in rugby). The Yale delegates insisted that 11-man squads would make for a more wide-open and exciting brand of play, and this suggestion was later adopted. Over the next few years, more tinkering would be done on and off the field. Slowly but surely a game as American as rugby is British would emerge.

Let the Game Begin

On hand for that momentous 1875 match between Harvard and Yale was young Walter Camp, who had grown up in New Haven and would matriculate at Yale the next year. Though his team was thoroughly outclassed, he was dazzled by the skill of the Harvard players, and was overwhelmed by the potential he saw in the game. Over the next few years, Camp took it upon himself to move football forward. He saw the game as being uniquely American, and wanted to make it even more so. During its rugbylike beginnings, football was a game of quickness and timing; Camp wanted to see more body contact, more hard tackling, and more violence. In his mind, these attributes—when combined with advances in speed, skill, and strategies—would make football the most breathtaking game on earth. In 1879, Camp refereed a game between Yale and Princeton—he was Yale's top player and captain, and at that time it was common for captains to assume "judge" duties. During this contest, Princeton resurrected the old interference ploy by putting two men slightly ahead of the ball carrier to clear a path for him. Camp warned the players that this violated the offside rule, adopted from rugby, which specifically stated that no one could move ahead of the ball. The concept, however, intrigued him. Later in the season, Yale reportedly used this play.

Although Camp lobbied hard for the rules changes he believed would make football better, it was not until 1880 that the Intercollegiate Football Association began to adopt his ideas. In that year, teams were reduced to 11 men per side, and the size of the field was reduced to 110 by 53 yards—very close to its present dimensions—and yard lines made their first appearance. The most important change, however, was the establishment of "scrimmage." In rugby, each play is initiated when the ball is thrown into a group of opposing players, and possession is determined by which side is able to kick the ball backwards to one of its own players. In 1880, at Camp's suggestion, this disorganized "scrummage" method was abandoned in favor of the current "scrimmage," whereby the team that starts with the ball gets it again after its player is tackled. This meant that teams could have set plays, and almost overnight made the role of team captain one of intellectual as well as physical skill.

In 1880 and 1881, a problem arose that threatened to squeeze the life out of the game. In those early days, it was customary in many sports to break a tie by awarding victory to the team or individual that had won the year before. What happened in football was that the teams that had won meetings a year earlier simply froze the football. They did not attempt to advance it, endeavoring only to protect it. This made for some boring contests, and agitated the growing crowds who were coming out to see what this new sport was all about. In 1882, Camp was instrumental in instituting a system of "downs," which forced a team to advance the ball or give it up after a certain number of plays. Originally, a team had three chances to make 5 yards; if a team lost 10 yards, however, it got three more downs. Some believe this rule marked the true beginning of modern football, for it brought with it new tactics and new strategies.

By 1882, a game somewhat similar to today's football was beginning to take shape. A team put seven men on its forward line—not bunched together but spread apart by as much as six feet per man. They stood straight up instead of crouching (contact below the waist was illegal), ready to do battle with their defensive counterparts. The center snapped the ball with his foot to one of three "halfbacks," who were so named because they stood halfway back. It would be a few more years before centers hiked the ball through their legs, as they do today. Needless to say, the foot snap took a lot of practice. The man taking the snap would

SETTLING THE SCORE

One of the last remnants of football's rugby roots was its complex scoring system. While a ball kicked between the goal posts from the field was worth four points and a touchdown only one, four points scored on touchdowns were given more weight than four points scored on one kicked goal. If a game ended in a tie, victory could be decided by safeties, if one team had four less than its opponent. At the time, safeties were so common that no points were awarded to the team tackling a ball carrier behind his own goal line. This weird scoring style caused a major ruckus in 1882, when Harvard and Princeton each scored one touchdown and kicked one field goal. Harvard claimed victory, insisting that its goal was much more valuable than Princeton's, which had been scored on the try awarded after its touchdown. Princeton disagreed, pointing to the high degree of difficulty of the kick. The referee awarded the game to Harvard, but Princeton refused to accept the decision and the game went into the books back in New Jersey as a victory. This kind of chaos drove Walter Camp crazy, so at the 1883 convention he introduced a set scoring system. Safeties, he proposed, would count for one point, touchdowns for two, goals kicked after a touchdown for four, and goals kicked from the field for five. The following year the values were altered to give more weight to touchdowns, and within a couple of decades the present scoring system (six points for a touchdown, three for a field goal, two for a safety or conversion play, and one for a kick after touchdown) was in use.

become the "quarterback," who actually moved up a bit to receive the ball a quarter of the way back. He was not allowed to advance the ball, nor was he allowed to throw it forward. He could, however, shuttle it to one of his halfbacks, or to the "fullback," so named because he started fully back. Some teams played two fullbacks. Others used the same player at quarterback on almost every play. There was not much imagination to play-calling. Most teams just picked a hole and tried to run the ball through the line.

In 1882, Yale tried something new to take advantage of the new five-yard rule. The team found that it could retain possession of the ball for very long periods of time by mixing short, powerful line plunges with pitch-out and lateral plays. This required fairly sophisticated blocking, but the element of mystery and the added movement really seemed to captivate fans, and the players liked it, too. By 1883, almost every team in the country was experimenting with this revolutionary idea, and the modern running game was born. In some ways, the best runners then were quite similar to today's top stars. They were fast, shifty, and adept at breaking tackles. But in addition to their running duties, they had to be able to kick. If a ball carrier saw the defense pinching in, he might punt the ball over their heads in an attempt to pin them deep in their own territory. Unlike today, a punt was a loose ball that could be recovered by either team, so there was always the chance the ball might be recovered by a teammate. A really good punter could loft the ball to a teammate who was running down the field—a play regarded as the forerunner of today's "bomb" pass. If a team got to within 20 or 30 yards of the goal line, the ball carrier might be asked to attempt a drop-kick. This kick did

not have to be executed from behind the line of scrimmage. In fact, a player could kick the ball on the dead run if he got close enough to the goal posts, which were 18'6" apart and 10' off the ground. A goal from the field, or "field goal," was usually the highlight of the game.

As the 1880s wore on the game's best minds began to focus their attention on blocking, or "guarding" as it was called in football's early days. This had almost always been a part of the American game, even when it was a soccerlike affair. But its potential had yet to be fully realized. In the open field, blockers typically ran alongside a ball carrier, waiting to grab, shove, punch, and otherwise interfere with anyone who got near him. But because the old rugby offsides rule was still on the books, they were careful not to pass the player with the ball. Also at the start of plays, offensive linemen did not crouch as they do today, but stood with their feet wide apart and their arms outstretched, ready to spar with oncoming defenders. By the mid-1880s, downfield blockers were beginning to get out in front of the ball, flattening defenders with a well-placed shoulder. And linemen were starting to become a bit more aggressive. By the late 1880s, the rugby-inspired offsides rule was being completely ignored by both players and referees and blocking was all the rage.

Opposing these early offensive formations were seven forward defensive linemen, and it was at about this time that some of these positions first got their names. The players on either end were called, predictably, "ends" and the man in the middle was called the "center." The players inside the ends were called "next to ends," until someone noticed that they made most of the tackles, and they were renamed "tacklers," which eventually became the present-day "tackles." The players next to center were called "next to centers"; eventually, they would end up playing slightly in back of their teammates on the line, becoming "linebackers."

Teams typically had 11 men who played both offense and defense, rarely missing a down. When severe injuries did occur, there were usually one or two substitutes available. Prior to games, teams practiced for an hour a day and ran in the gymnasium to build up endurance. It is interesting to note that as football changed during the 1880s so too did the young men who played it. A typical college player might have been 5'4" and 140 pounds back in the 1870s. But as football became more of a contact sport, these players were replaced by slower, less agile six-footers who carried a lot more bulk on their frames.

Leading by example, the "Big Three"—Harvard, Yale, and Princeton—made football the hottest game on America's college campuses during the 1880s, even surpassing baseball in popularity. Among the many schools fielding teams were Amherst, Brown, Bucknell, California, City College of New York, Cornell, Dartmouth, Dickinson, Fordham, Haverford, Indiana, Johns Hopkins, Lafayette, Lehigh, Massachusetts Institute of Technology, Michigan, Minnesota, the Naval Academy, Notre Dame, Penn State, Pennsylvania, Purdue, Southern California, Stevens, Swarthmore, Trinity, Tufts, Union, Virginia, Virginia Military Institute, Washington, Washington & Lee, Wesleyan, and Williams.

Mass Appeal

In 1888 the Intercollegiate Football Association passed two rules that transformed football into little more than a contest of brute strength and endurance. The first rule forbid offensive blockers to extend their arms and shove or grab a defender. The second allowed defensive players to hit below the waist. The new tackling rule virtually shut down the offensive game. Coaches who had spent the early 1880s developing basic running plays suddenly found them ineffective. These plays had been designed to get a runner out in the open, where he could twist away from opponents trying to grab at his upper body—now a lone tackler could bring down the most elusive runner by simply wrapping his arms around his legs. A quick ball carrier could still find daylight, but not as much of it, and not nearly as often.

On the front line, the situation was even worse. Offensive linemen could no longer stand upright, because defenders could easily cut their legs out from under them and simply continue on into the backfield. To counteract this move, offensive linemen began to assume a crouch position similar to the one used today. They also had to move closer together—shoulder-to-shoulder, in fact—because of the no-hands rule. Prior to 1888, a defender trying to cut between two blockers could simply be grabbed, shoved to the ground, or "clothes-lined" with a strategically placed arm to the head. Now defenders were coming in low and hard, and blockers had to use their bodies and shoulders instead of their arms to stop them. Whereas offensive lines had stretched across 50 feet or more during the early and middle 1880s, after 1888 a team's front line might be only 20 feet across—even tighter than today's formations. With their blockers all squeezed into a confined space, the runners of the day were forced to pinch in,

PUDGE TAKES FLIGHT

What makes a football game or any other athletic contest memorable is an individual's incredible feat, a ball's improbable bounce—in other words, a great play. The first great play preserved in the annals of football history happened as one team tried to stop the fearsome V-trick, or wedge, play. In 1888, Princeton unveiled it against Yale on the second-half kickoff. The Tigers put seven men on the outer flank of its wedge, and crowded four more (including the man with the ball) inside the V. Yale's Pudge Heffelfinger, the biggest, strongest player of the 19th century, got up a good head of steam and propelled himself right at the leading point of the wedge. He leaped high in the air, cleared the front wall of crouching players, and landed on the four Princeton men in the middle, flattening all of them including the ball carrier!

Heffelfinger was one of the game's first great blockers. He could move straight ahead and blow great holes in an opponent's forward wall, or pull back from his position and loop around end to lead the interference on outside running plays. The latter technique he learned from teammate George Woodruff, who was every bit as good as Heffelfinger from a technical standpoint, although not nearly as large. Woodruff later used his expertise in line play to devise revolutionary formations while coaching at Penn in the 1890s. Led by Heffelfinger, Woodruff, and Captain Pa Corbin, the Elis turned in a perfect season in 1888, shutting out every team they faced. One of the top runners on the team was a young man named Amos Alonzo Stagg. Like Woodruff, he was a good player made great by his understanding of the game.

too. They started each play close to the quarterback for their own protection.

Although no one intended it to happen, the style of football that had captured the nation's imagination had disappeared. To this day it is unclear what the rulesmakers had in mind when they enacted these changes. By all accounts, they were quite satisfied with football as it was: a wide-open game, with lots of running and lateraling and kicking. Yet almost immediately, football transformed itself into an ugly, brutal sport.

Ironically, the man to blame may have been Walter Camp. It had always been his intention to make football a rougher game—and it was he who first proposed the new tackling rule—but it is hard to believe that Camp would have done so had he known what would follow.

With offenses massed together, the game's strategists turned their attention to devising plays that made best use of this mass. The first was simple: create a wall of six or seven blockers, run right at the de-

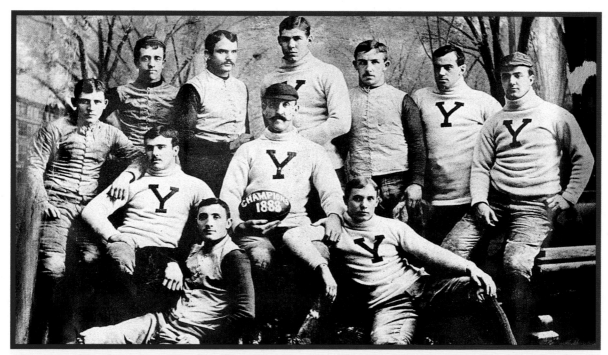

The 1888 Yale team, coached by Walter Camp and starring (back row, from left) Amos Alonzo Stagg, William Rhodes, George Woodruff, Pudge Heffelfinger, and (sitting with football) captain William ("Pa") Corbin. The Elis went 13–0 and outscored opponents 698-0.

fense, and bulldoze as many players as possible so that the ball carrier might spring free. The problem with this scheme was that a single tackler could slip between two men and bring down the ball carrier with relative ease. Princeton's answer was to resurrect a formation first attempted by Lehigh a few years earlier: the V-trick. It featured a wedge-shaped wall of blockers surrounding the man with the ball. It was much more difficult to slice in between blockers in this formation, especially when they linked arms and started moving forward. It was a slow, methodical play, and it was perfect for kickoffs, which worked a bit differently 110 years ago. Since all kicks were considered live balls, the team kicking off did not boot the ball as far as it could. Instead, it nudged

it an inch or two, picked it up and ran at what today would be considered the "receiving" team. The players would form a V around the ball carrier and move slowly downfield. When the teams met, a big pileup ensued, and if the play worked correctly the runner would break out of the wedge as it began to disintegrate and make his way upfield for a few more yards. This play became the standard kickoff strategy within a couple of seasons.

It soon became clear to everyone who understood football that, given the new rules, new plays had to be concocted to put as many blockers between the ball carrier and the defense as possible. In 1890, Amos Alonzo Stagg—who had graduated from Yale and accepted a job at the YMCA

College in Springfield, Illinois—devised an offensive set he called "Ends Back." As the name implies, the ends were moved from the line of scrimmage into the backfield, where they could get a running start as blockers. The ball was snapped to the quarterback, the ends crashed into the line in an attempt to move the pile forward, and then the ball carrier would follow. The other backs might plow into the line, too, or protect the runner's flanks from tacklers coming around the pile. Each play was a test of strength and a lesson in pain—if you happened to fall and were trampled by the pile, you just covered up and hoped to come out alive.

Stagg, however, had a mind for more than brute-force plays. He also used his Ends Back formation to spring a runner outside, as five men were available to run interference. This play, which to today's fans might seem an obvious outgrowth of a five-man backfield, won Stagg much acclaim. In 1891, he befuddled both Harvard and Yale with this formation, and this accomplishment earned him a job at the University of Chicago. At Chicago, Stagg began experimenting with all sorts of backfield trickery, including reverse plays and even double-reverses. In all, he came up with at least 40 brand-new football plays, many of which survive to this day.

A college team demonstrates the punishing V-trick or wedge play, in which players surrounding the ball carrier would link arms and attempt to plow through the defense.

As football become ever more ugly and dangerous, Stagg's ideas were met with enthusiasm. Philip King, who had distinguished himself as a top player and strategist with Princeton in the early 1890s, returned to school as a graduate student and (as the rules of the day allowed) managed to squeeze in a little more football. King brought his ends off the line, too, but positioned them farther away from the quarterback, out on the wings. From this formation, he designed new plays that caught several top teams completely by surprise, including powerful Yale.

Unfortunately, the intricate criss-crosses and fakes designed by Stagg, King, and others could not undo the gridlock that was ruining football. These plays were extremely difficult to execute; even Stagg's own players messed them up, especially late in games, when they were nearing exhaustion. Stagg did devise one play, however, that seemed to work no matter how tired his players were: the "Turtleback." This was a formation that blended the worst of 1890s football with the best of modern backfield strategy. After the ball was snapped, the offensive team quickly formed a tight oval around the ball carrier. This wheel of humanity would then start "rolling" to the left or right, using the tackle as its stationary point. The players would then unravel down the field, with each player blocking a defensive man until the man with the ball was on his own. This was not a fast play, but a slow methodical one—and an altogether bizarre one by modern standards. The players would hunch over, forming the turtle's back, protecting the ball carrier from the defensive players who were hurling themselves at the oval in an attempt to break it apart. This was a much easier play to run

than any of the complex criss-crosses Stagg devised, and thus was the one that most other coaches copied. By 1893, several top schools were using the Turtleback, as well as other mass-momentum formations. For his part, Stagg always lamented introducing the Turtleback, and even accepted partial blame for the sad state of football in the early 1890s.

In defense of Stagg, the Turtleback was tame in comparison to the "Flying Wedge." This play, which was a more elaborate and dangerous version of the V-trick, was introduced to the world by Harvard in 1892. Ironically, it was invented by chess expert Lorin Deland, who had never played a down of football in his life. Instead of bunching together prior to kickoff, the Harvard players spread themselves across the field in two lines. At the captain's signal, they began running at full speed toward the ball, converging at a full gallop to form a moving wedge around the ball carrier. It was not unusual for this formation to plow through the defense for 30 yards before it was stopped, and it was stopped only at considerable risk to life and limb. And of course, anyone unlucky enough to be trampled by this pack would be lucky to emerge with anything less than a concussion.

By the 1893 season, every team in the country was using the Flying Wedge. Injuries reached shocking levels. The play was considered so dangerous that the Army and Navy agreed to cancel their annual football game in 1894 for fear that too many men would be lost. At the University of Pennsylvania, George Woodruff taught his players to employ the "flying" principal to all of their blocks, taking a running start before the ball was snapped and crashing into helpless linemen. Other teams followed suit, and injuries reached appalling proportions.

At the end of the 1893 season, the University Athletic Club of New York invited representatives of the Harvard, Yale, Princeton, and Penn football teams to meet with Paul Dashiell, at the time the recognized dean of football officials. The members of the club, a great majority of whom were former players, were gravely concerned that their game was headed for extinction. They convinced the schools to rewrite the rules so as to remove much of the danger and brutality. All forms of the wedge were outlawed, as were plays that sent four or more blockers smashing into the line ahead of the ball carrier. The length of games was reduced from 90 to 70 minutes, and tackling anyone but the ball carrier—a growing problem in the sport—was prohibited. The kickoff rule was altered to its modern form, giving the receiving team a chance to receive the ball, and a third official was added to the standard two-man crew.

The intentions of this group were good, but football was not about to become a safer game. Immediately, coaches such as Camp, Stagg, and Woodruff found ways to circumvent the rules. They took their biggest, heaviest linemen and moved them into the backfield, where they could get a running start before delivering their blocks. Woodruff's Penn team was the most successful of the mid-1890s thanks to a play that sent two gigantic guards crashing through the same hole, one behind the other, in front of the ball carrier. This "Guards Back" play brought the school three straight national championships, and no one would find a way to stop the play until the end of the century. In the interim, dozens of opponents suffered serious injuries when they bore the

brunt of this double-barreled blocking scheme.

To further underscore the brutish character of football during the 1890s, remember that football was then a two-way game—the behemoths executing these sledgehammer offenses were the same guys who had to stop it when the ball changed hands. And they attempted to do so with the same level of savagery. As hard as the offensive line might try to "move the pile," the defensive line moved it right back. And defensive backs, spotting openings in the line, would get up a head of steam and try to blow past blockers and meet a ball carrier before he got going. Walter Camp found an ingenious way to deal with this style of defense: he instructed his linemen to allow a charging defensive back entry into the line and then bump him in one direction. This created a hole for a running back coming from the other direction. This "trap" play is still used today.

Critics of college football continued to find it too dangerous, and fans were growing weary of the pileups that still characterized most plays. There were periodic outcries to somehow ban all mass play. The Ivy League schools that had given birth to football continued to tinker with the rules, trying to make the game safer. The most important change was the requirement that a set number of men play up on the line; the idea was to curtail mass play, but as always the smart coaches found a way around the rule and the dumb ones simply copied them. Princeton's King, for instance, designed a suped-up version of the Turtleback called the "Revolving Tandem," which formed quickly after the ball was snapped, and rolled down the field at a much faster pace than Stagg's plodding formation. It seemed

Yale and Harvard square off across the line of scrimmage. The intense football rivalry between these Ivy League schools got underway in 1875.

that whatever rules were instituted to make the game safer, someone always found a legal way to make it more dangerous.

Nothing about football suggested that it was the gentleman's game it had once been. And colleges at the turn of the century saw themselves as being in the business of turning out young gentlemen who were ready to assume important leadership roles in the future. As a result, in the years between 1894 and 1905, several colleges shut down their football programs. Despite new rules and equipment introduced in the name of safety, there were still too many injuries, too many fights, too much senseless brutality, and too much cheating.

The Early Pros

During the 19th century, one of the places a young college graduate could make the right connections was in a local athletic club. It was a good way to stay fit, compete with other young men, and make business connections with some of the older members. These clubs typically had gymnasiums for winter workouts and rented fields in the spring to play baseball or hold track and field competitions. In the fall, most clubs turned to soccer or some other "safe" activity. A few clubs, however, played football. Their games were similar in style to college contests, with a couple of important exceptions. First, the players were a little older, a little bigger, and a little slower. Second, a star player fresh out of college—or even a brawny local kid—could make a big difference in the outcome of a game, because there was usually a wide range of talent on the field. It was not uncommon for a club to bring in a "ringer" for an important game—the only problem was that the clubs, which were members of the Amateur Athletic Union, could not pay these imported stars without breaking AAU rules.

The solution was a system of compensation that satisfied everyone, yet technically did not violate the rules of the Amateur Athletic Union. After a game, a star player would receive a gold watch or some other piece of hardware as a "trophy." Next, he would take it to a local pawn shop and get a loan for, say, $25, then sell the pawn ticket to a club member for another $25, and he would go back to school with $50 in his pocket. The club member would go to the pawn shop, pay the broker $25 for the item, and bring it back to the club. The following week, the same player might receive the same pocket watch and the whole scheme went back into motion.

During the 1890s, an "elite" level of club football teams developed, principally in western Pennsylvania. In the towns where these clubs operated, the local folk adopted the football team as their own, and attended games in huge numbers. Some even accompanied their team when they played on the road, against other clubs, or occasionally in exhibitions against college teams. These fans were every bit as boisterous as the college crowds, and they often bet heavily on their boys—which understandably raised their passion to a fever pitch. A victory was cause for great celebra-

tion and generated enormous civic pride, while a defeat was considered a blight upon the losing town. Local merchants and politicians—many of whom were members of these athletic clubs—gladly supported the local football team, whether it meant chipping in a few dollars to secure the services of a top college player, or arranging for a high-paying job for a talented graduate. The clubs were happy to go along with this chicanery, for there was a direct correlation between the success of a club's football team and the number of people interested in becoming members—and thus the amount of dues flowing into the club treasury.

After graduating from Yale in 1892, Pudge Heffelfinger was a man much in demand. Every fan in the country knew his name and had heard of his collegiate exploits. His presence on the playing field guaranteed a huge crowd—a fact of which he was well aware. In November, Heffelfinger cut a deal with the Allegheny Athletic Association to play against its archrival, the Pittsburgh Athletic Club. Toward the end of the game, Pudge jarred loose a fumble, scooped it up, and ran for the winning touchdown. As agreed, he and two football-playing friends who accompanied him were handed twice their train fare. Club records, now on display at the Pro Football Hall of Fame, also clearly show that Heffelfinger was slipped an extra $500—a huge sum in those days.

Thrilled with this financial windfall and anxious to cash in on his fame, Heffelfinger hooked up with the Chicago Athletic Club for football's first barnstorming tour. The team played six games in 12 days, picking up local players when injuries occurred and taking on opponents ranging from the Case School (a prep school) to Harvard and

Princeton. Pudge proved a huge drawing card, and fans came out in droves just to catch a glimpse of him. How much did he pocket for his troubles? Heffelfinger claimed that he accepted nothing more than expense money for this grueling trip. Of course, he never admitted accepting that first $500 from the Allegheny club, either.

After the success of the Heffelfinger experiment, the Allegheny club continued to compensate star players through 1893 and 1894, drawing enough attention through their "under the table" dealings to provoke an 1895 AAU investigation into their hiring of amateurs. With scrutiny focused on them, the AAA simply decided not to field a football team.

By this time, other clubs in western Pennsylvania were hiring top players. The Greensburg Athletic Association paid former Princetonian Lawton Fiscus $20 a contest and demolished all of its 1894 opponents. In 1895, a surge of civic pride in nearby Latrobe led the local newspaper to sponsor a football team to knock rival Greensburg off its perch. As its season opener approached, the team was still without a competent quarterback. A talented high schooler named John Brallier was hired for $10 plus expenses, and he led Latrobe to a 12-0 victory over a club from the town of Jeannette. For many years, Brallier was believed to be the first professional—in fact, the National Football League later honored him with a lifetime pass. Within weeks, the Duquesne Country and Athletic Club began openly hiring players, drawing so many fans that at season's end the club showed a $4,000 profit.

The Allegheny Athletic Association, meanwhile, learned that it would be tossed out of the AAU because of its past use of pros. Ironically, by its actions the country's leading amateur organization turned out to be an unwitting accomplice in the establishment of professional football. The Allegheny club accepted its ejection and decided to field a team in 1896. Free of AAU meddling, the Alleghenys openly recruited the best players available, including Heffelfinger, ex-Princeton star Ben "Sport" Donnelly, and former Penn star George Brooke. They destroyed the Duquesne and Pittsburgh clubs on consecutive days, estab-

Ed Abbaticchio, "Mr. Punt." The brilliant kicker and fullback starred for Latrobe in the 1890s, but found he could make a better living playing baseball. He is pictured here in his Boston Nationals uniform.

lishing themselves as the top team in football's most competitive city.

The first team to have an owner was the Duquesne club, which saw its football payroll rise dramatically when it outbid other teams for players returning from the Spanish-American War in 1898. To the rescue came club member William Temple, who assumed responsibility for the club's football operation. Temple, a leader in the steel industry, was crazy for sports, and he loved being associated with winners. The Duquesne football team went undefeated for two years. Its personnel, payroll, and level of organization so outclassed other teams in the region that there was some question as to whether anyone—including the top colleges—could give Temple's team a decent game. Temple's competitors in the steel industry soon tired of hearing his name whenever conversation turned to football, and in 1900 fellow steel magnate A. C. Dinkey raided Temple's club, hiring his key players to perform for his club, the Homestead Library and Athletic Club. For the next two years, it was Dinkey's name that was associated with the city's best football team.

In 1902, Connie Mack, manager and part-owner of baseball's Philadelphia Athletics, organized a football team made up of the top players in Philadelphia, as well as some of the ballplayers on his major-league baseball team. Not one to be outdone (and still stinging from Mack's signing of his star second baseman, Napoleon Lajoie), Philadelphia Phillies owner Art Rogers also put together a team. Across the state in Pittsburgh, Pirates owner Barney Dreyfuss got into the action by hiring away the top players from the Duquesne and Homestead clubs. The three baseball owners agreed to

form a three-team league, which they named the National Football League. Dave Berry, the Latrobe newspaperman who had hired Brallier as his quarterback seven years earlier, was himself hired to act as commissioner of this new league. Players reportedly earned between $400 and $1,200 for the season.

This first NFL had plenty of star power. Pittsburgh's top runner was former Bucknell football star Christy Mathewson, who also happened to pitch for the New York Giants. Connie Mack put his star pitcher (and noted screwball) Rube Waddell on his roster, mainly so he could keep him out of trouble during the off-season. The teams played each other, as well as outside clubs—the problem was that they didn't play the same number of games, nor did they play the same opponents. At season's end, both the Athletics and Pittsburgh had similar records and laid claim to the NFL title, and much bickering ensued.

For their part, the players could not have cared less. In fact, on New Year's Day the top stars of the Phillies and Athletics went ahead and re-formed into a team representing the city of New York so they could enter themselves in an indoor "World Series" of football held in Madison Square Garden. Ironically, the pros were beaten by the Syracuse Athletic Club, which featured a young guard by the name of Pop Warner.

The organizers of the NFL abandoned plans to schedule a 1903 season, and many of the league's stars were signed by a team from the western Pennsylvania town of Franklin. The town's citizens were smarting from a 1902 loss to longtime rival Oil City, and a local promoter named Billy Prince was charged with assembling an unbeatable team. Prince did such a good job that Oil

City refused to play Franklin. Franklin won all of its games that season and did not give up a single point. And it kept its perfect record intact at the second (and last) football World Series in New York, winning the championship easily.

Because Franklin had a near monopoly on western Pennsylvania's best players, other teams in the area did not see the point of hiring those who were left. So several top performers ventured west to Ohio and joined the Massillon Tigers, who beat Akron for the 1903 state championship. The following year, other Ohio teams tried to outbid Massillon for top players, siphoning off many more of Pennsylvania's best play-

ers and decimating pro football in that state. Among these men was halfback Charles Follis of the Shelby Athletic Club, football's first black professional.

Massillon won the state championship again in 1904, prompting the formation of the Canton Bulldogs for the 1905 season. Like Greensburg and Latrobe in Pennsylvania, the towns of Canton and Massillon had a long-standing rivalry in both commerce and sports. Massillon was willing to do whatever it took to defend its two football championships, and Canton's backers vowed to spare no expense in dethroning the Tigers. What ensued was a bidding war between two tiny towns that rocked the

Canton and Massillon in a 1919 game. In 1905 and 1906 these neighboring Ohio small towns were the center of the pro football world, as they dueled each other in a bidding war for the best players.

football world. Salaries skyrocketed, attracting the best players in the country. Canton focused on creating a high-powered offense, and even signed University of Michigan superstar Willie Heston for $600 to play in the game against Massillon. Massillon concentrated on recruiting top defensive players. This strategy prevailed, as the Tigers won the big showdown 14-4. Heston was completely shut down, prompting many to proclaim the still-obscure pro game to be far superior to the much heralded college game.

In 1906, the two teams continued to compete for the nation's top stars, but the stakes had become incredibly high for these tiny towns. Professional gamblers often descended upon their games, and hundreds of thousands of dollars were being bet on and against them. Whispers that members of both teams were on the take were heard all season long. With so much attention trained on them, Canton and Massillon began to feel the heat.

In the first of their two meetings that year, the Bulldogs dethroned the Tigers 10-5, handing them their first loss in three years. Massillon took back the championship in their second match by a score of 13-6. After the game, allegations that Canton coach Blondy Wallace had thrown the game were printed in the Massillon newspaper. Canton accused Massillon of concocting the story to hurt attendance at its next game, against Latrobe, which it did; the stands were nearly empty. Without the anticipated gate receipts, Canton could not pay its players. This effectively destroyed the Bulldogs' credibility when it came to signing stars for 1907, and without Canton as an archenemy Massillon could not draw enough fans to afford its players either.

Whether the gambling story was true or not, it effectively stopped the progress of pro football. It would be a long time before the game would again see two teams of such high quality.

College Football 1905–20

Pro football's problems in the early parts of this century were only compounded by the controversy surrounding the college game. The game's increasing brutality and reliance on mass play was producing a shocking number of serious injuries. In 1905 alone, 18 college-football deaths were reported. President Theodore Roosevelt summoned representatives from Harvard, Yale, and Princeton to the White House at mid-season and told them that he would abolish the sport altogether if he did not see some dramatic changes. This meeting was followed by a two-part conference at New York University, where sweeping reforms were made by representatives from more than 60 schools. The second conference saw the formation of the Intercollegiate Athletic Association (IAA), the forerunner of the National Collegiate Athletic Association (NCAA).

Under the leadership of Walter Camp and Army's Palmer Pierce, the convention established new guidelines that opened up the game and banned dangerous play. The yardage required for a first down was doubled from 5 to 10, forcing teams to find a more productive way to gain ground than simply smashing into the line. A neutral zone was established at the line of scrimmage, putting a foot or so between the brutes who had formerly lined up nose-to-nose. Linemen had to play on the line,

Cornell, I yell, yell, yell, Cornell

CORNELL

By the early 1900s football had been embraced by colleges across the country, and students belted out fight songs to cheer on their teams.

which kept them from getting a running start. Games were shortened from 70 to 60 minutes, and yet another official was added—all in the name of safer football. Almost immediately, football became more watchable. The constant fistfights and squabbling over offsides that had been holding up games were virtually eliminated when the linemen were separated, and although teams still tried to send two and three blockers into the same hole, it wasn't as effective. Mass play had finally been curtailed.

Ultimately, the most important of the new rules was the little-noticed legalization of the forward pass. The spirit of the pass-

ing rule was to clear the gridlock at the line of scrimmage, which traditionally gave an unfair advantage to the team that put the biggest bodies on the field. By utilizing the pass, a quick, smart team could go around or over a big, clumsy one—something that could not have happened prior to 1906.

Coaches did not immediately embrace the passing game, and for good reason. It was a risky play—the rules at the time treated an incomplete pass as a live ball, just like a fumble. And the odds were against completing a high percentage. The old watermelon-shaped ball (a whopping nine inches "fatter" than the modern ball) was extremely hard to throw with any zip and

The melon-shaped footballs used in the sport's early years were nine inches fatter than the modern ball and were extremely difficult to throw.

accuracy; furthermore, no one really knew exactly *how* to throw it. Lastly, coaches had to consider how to incorporate the pass into their offenses, work out some effective plays, and teach their teams to execute them.

The first team to tinker exensively with an aerial attack was St. Louis University. Coach Eddie Cochems, long an advocate of legalizing the forward pass, came to St. Louis in 1906 and at a special preseason camp he schooled halfback Brad Robinson in the art of throwing and end Jack Schneider in the art of receiving. This was no easy task. Cochems spent a long time studying the aerodynamic properties of the football, and it was he who determined the best place

to hold it and the proper wrist action to send it on its way. St. Louis's new passing play was unveiled during the team's opener against Carroll College. By the time St. Louis met the University of Iowa's powerful team, Robinson and Schneider were unstoppable. They defeated the Hawkeyes 39-0, and caused great excitement with their expertise. St. Louis won all of its games that year, and outscored opponents by the eye-popping margin of 402-11.

Until St. Louis showed the way, most football watchers thought the crude method of passing developed by Harvard and Yale—who used the new weapon sparingly, just to keep defenses from throwing all 11 men at their ball carriers—was the correct one. The passer would wait until his intended receiver had arrived at a predetermined spot, and then loft the ball high in the air. While it was floating above the field, blockers would clear all the defensive players away from the receiver, who would then be free to catch it. The Ivy Leaguers were shocked when they heard that someone out in St. Louis was hitting a lone receiver on the dead run. Yet despite the news from St. Louis, most teams in the East were uninterested in learning the forward pass. The game they played was still based on line plunges, power blocking, punting, and either overpowering opponents or waiting for them to make a mistake. At a time when a team had just three downs to move the ball 10 yards, it was considered too risky to waste one of those downs on a pass play.

In the Midwest, however, a couple of coaches took notice. Chicago's Amos Alonzo Stagg was an immediate fan of the forward pass, diagramming nine basic passing plays that are still in use today. More than a decade earlier he had had a quarterback named Frank Hering, who could throw long overhand laterals to his teammates. Stagg used this play primarily on kickoffs, with Hering whipping the ball across the field just as opposing tacklers converged on him. This gave him the idea for a play he called the "Double Pass," which involved one player throwing a long lateral to a teammate, and then taking off down the field for a return pass. At the Carlisle Indian School in Pennsylvania, coach Pop Warner taught his players to fake a pass and then run with the ball, and they used this play with great success. Meanwhile, at the University of Illinois, quarterback Pomeroy Sinnock became the first player to truly master the spiral toss.

The only place passing met with immediate acceptance and widespread use in 1906 was at the high school level, and this is where the most experimentation occurred. High school coaches longing to move up to the college ranks worked feverishly to unlock the mysteries of the forward pass, and players hoping to earn college scholarships worked tirelessly to perfect their throwing skills. This had a great effect on college football, for the freshmen of 1907 had already mastered a skill that still mystified their upperclassmates. By 1908, most colleges had worked at least a dozen different pass plays into their offenses, but because

Amos Alonzo Stagg, coach at the University of Chicago, was a creative and prolific offensive strategist who pioneered scores of basic plays in use to this day.

INTO THE PASSING LANE

One of the high school players who "grew up" with the new forward pass was a young man of Norwegian descent named Knute Rockne. Although he weighed just 140 pounds when he played for Northwest Division High School in Chicago, he was fast, tough, and a quick learner. Upon graduation in 1910, Rockne set his sights on a career in chemistry. At the suggestion of friends, he enrolled at a small Catholic university in South Bend, Indiana, called Notre Dame. It was a good school of about 500 students, and it had excellent athletic facilities. The football team was nothing to brag about, but at least he would have a chance to make the starting squad.

Rockne played well in 1911 and 1912, but Notre Dame mostly played other small colleges. On the schedule for 1913, however, was the United States Military Academy, which had one of the top teams in the country. Army had scheduled the game with the little Midwestern school as a tune-up for the stiffer competition it would face that November. It never occurred to anyone—least of all to Notre Dame's own players—that there was even a remote chance they could win. But with the new passing rules of 1910 and 1912 in place, coach Jesse Harper believed he could ambush Army.

In June 1913—before Rockne and his roommate, Gus Dorias, left for their summer jobs as lifeguards— Harper told them to spend every free minute tossing a football around. Over the next three months the two young men did just that, developing a real feel for the aerial game. When they returned to school in the fall, coach Harper handed

of the risk involved only a few programs passed the ball enough to be effective. By 1910, every player in the college ranks had been fully exposed to the forward pass, and long passes were occasionally deciding games.

Walter Camp, who had originally urged legalization of the forward pass, feared that the game was about to become too wide-open. As the leading member of the IAA rules committee, he urged that the passing game be severely curtailed and possibly eliminated altogether. To his dismay, he and

his supporters lost this battle, and in 1910 a series of rules were instituted that further encouraged the throwing of the football. Most important among them was that pass receivers could no longer be hit while the ball was in the air. Interestingly, a rule limiting the length of passes to 20 yards was also added for a couple of seasons, mostly because an effective scheme for pass coverage had yet to be developed. In 1912 a fourth down was added, giving cautious teams more incentive to risk passing the football. And end zones came into being so that balls

them a new playbook chock-full of passing plays. Notre Dame would take full advantage of the new passing rules, he explained, and maybe—just maybe—they could beat Army.

In its first three games, Notre Dame unveiled its spectacular new aerial attack, racking up 169 points. Rockne all but invented the art of receiving, making sharp cuts, finding seams in the defense, changing speeds, and coming back to the ball. Notre Dame's other ends simply ran down the field, but because he had worked all summer with Dorias, Rockne was the one who proved impossible to cover. And whereas other receivers hugged the ball hard against their chests, Rockne mastered the skill of cradling it softly in his outstretched hands, and he could even pull in passes with one hand.

The Army game started as most fans expected. Each Army lineman was about 20 pounds heavier than the man he faced, and Army simply overwhelmed Notre Dame at the line of scrimmage. But when Notre Dame got the ball midway through the first quarter, Dorias informed his men that it was time to let Army have it. He calmly sidestepped Army's fierce rush and completed several short passes to his backs, then hummed a 40-yard pass to Rockne in the end zone for the game's first score. Army trailed by a point at halftime, but its men were expending tremendous amounts of energy grinding out tough yards on offense, and chasing Notre Dame's receivers all over the field on defense. In the third quarter, Army dropped several men into its defensive backfield, but Dorias crossed them up by running the ball through the weakened line. In the final quarter, Army dug in again at the line of scrimmage, and Dorias and Rockne picked them to pieces. The final score was 35-13, with all five Notre Dame touchdowns coming through the air. From that day forward, Notre Dame would be recognized as a football powerhouse.

caught past the goal line could be counted as touchdowns—previously, a player had to catch a pass and then run over the goal line for it to count. Schools such as Notre Dame (in 1913) and Oklahoma (in 1914 and 1915) rode aerial attacks to national prominence; the forward pass had proved to be a powerful new weapon in the arsenals of football strategists, and it was here to stay.

The drastic changes football underwent between 1906 and the late 1910s transformed it into an exciting, highly profitable sport. Colleges reaped tremendous revenues

and gained national attention from football, and star players served as poster boys for their schools. In a remarkably brief period of time, the image of the football player went from ruffian to America's ultimate role model. Men admired their daring and courage, women adored their dashing good looks, and kids wanted to be like them in every way. Football players began popping up in popular literature, especially in children's books. And thanks to newspapers, magazines, and annual guides, the names and faces of the nation's top juniors and seniors were almost as well known as those of baseball's top stars.

As the style of the game opened up, fans began to recognize and appreciate the skills of the best offensive players. In the old days, the big linemen were the players who dominated the games. The players who scored the touchdowns were well known, of course, but fans understood that they were only as good as the players blocking for them. Given that most plays ended in a gigantic pile-up, spectators were more likely to notice the big guy who tossed opponents around than the little guy who carried the ball into the fray. But with line play becoming part of the bigger offensive picture, fans

"Now hurry and change your clothes, my dear, and we'll go some place and dance!"

Dirty, bruised, and weary, the player in this illustration is nonetheless seen as an attractive social partner. By the close of the 1910s college players were regarded as all-American heroes instead of ruffians.

began to root for the great backs. Their ability to dart through the pile, scamper around end, and throw and receive passes made them the new "game-breakers." Linemen were no less important, of course, but they no longer commanded the attention they once did. The big names in the backfield during this era included Ted Coy, Jim Thorpe, Eddie Mahan, and George Gipp.

The hero of all young boys in the early part of the century was a fictional character named Frank Merriwell. Honest, good, strong, and brave, he also happened to excel at sports, always raising the level of his performance when the chips were down. Yale fullback Ted Coy came as close as any real-life athlete to achieving that mythical Merriwell status. He stood six feet tall and weighed just under 200 pounds. He wore a white sweatband, which kept a shock of boyish blond hair out of his eyes. And he was relentless. For three seasons (1907–1909), Coy took the ball play after play and pounded right into the line. During those years Yale lost just one game. He endured unimaginable punishment, at times reportedly bringing the crowd to tears. Yet he always had a funny remark or kind word for teammates, opponents, and referees. As a kicker, Coy was an unparalleled offensive force. He booted the ball long and especially high, drawing the *oohs* and *aahs* he loved so well. And he could drop-kick the ball off his instep (soccer-style), which meant he was a scoring threat even when he was moving laterally. On defense, his jarring tackles stopped many an enemy drive.

Thorpe, a member of Oklahoma's Sac and Fox tribe, entered the Carlisle Indian School at the age of 15 and proceeded to turn the obscure Pennsylvania industrial institution into the nation's premier football powerhouse. Thorpe was an astonishing player. He was the best kicker, blocker, and runner of his day, and a defensive dynamo, too. He had moves no one had ever seen before, and he could knock a man out with a simple straight-arm if he got in his way. Thorpe specialized in taking kicks on the run and then shredding an opponent's coverage. He tore off at least one long run in practically every game he played, including contests against the country's top teams. Ironically, Carlisle was never nationally ranked because it was more a vocational school than a college. In fact, some of Thorpe's teammates were 14 and 15, while others were in their mid-20s. But the team's amazing record speaks for itself: impressive wins against Harvard, Pennsylvania, Georgetown, Lafayette, Pittsburgh, Lehigh, Syracuse, and Army.

Mahan was as cool as they came. The Harvard star combined sharp eyes, quick feet, and explosive speed to slice his way through the slimmest openings. Once in the open field, he could beat almost any man one-on-one. Mahan was no less dangerous behind the line of scrimmage, where he passed with great accuracy and pinned opponents against their own goal line with his specialty, the coffin-corner kick. Mahan made a science of deceptive running, "giving" a tackler his right or left leg and then snapping it out of the way once the defender had committed himself. In an era when runners felt naked without a couple of big teammates in front of them, Mahan regularly cut away from his blockers or simply sped past them. He was one of the first backs to earn All-America recognition three years in a row, and was the star of stars on Harvard's undefeated 1914 team, which man-for-man might have been the school's best ever.

THE GREAT JIM THORPE

Jim Thorpe, one of football's first great offensive stars. An amazing athlete, Thorpe won two track-and-field gold medals at the 1912 Olympics and also played professional baseball.

Jim Thorpe attended the Carlisle Indian School in Pennsylvania, a trade school for Native American boys and girls that had been in operation since 1789. Carlisle was neither a high school nor a college, and its students ranged in age from 8 to 28. But it did have a good athletic program and competed against both high school and college teams in a variety of sports. The football team in particular was highly regarded.

In 1904 Carlisle's football coach, Pop Warner, spotted the teenaged Thorpe fooling around on the track. He could see that Thorpe had great athletic ability, but doubted whether he would make much of a football player. Still, he invited Thorpe to practice. Thorpe watched the others play for a few minutes, announced that no one could tackle him, and proceeded to run up and down the field at will, leaving a trail of writhing bodies in his wake.

Warner had himself an extraordinary player. Thorpe was as fast as anyone who had ever run the ball. His leaping ability was phenomenal, and he could drop-kick the ball more than 60 yards. In the open field, he was able to shift his hips to shake loose tacklers, and when he plowed through the line his massive shoulders cleared out defensive linemen like bowling pins. If someone was poised to get a grip on Thorpe, he earned himself a stiff-arm with enough force behind it to knock a man out.

Thorpe made his big-time debut against the powerful team from the University of Pennsylvania. He played like a man among boys, breaking off runs of 65 and 85 yards. He also caused several Penn players to be carried off the field after he buried them with vicious tackles. After one of his scoring romps in the shocking 26-6 win, Thorpe smiled at Warner and said, "This is fun."

Arguably this country's greatest all-around athlete, Thorpe stayed busy when he was not playing football. During his final year at Carlisle, he won five letters, and starred for the track, fencing, lacrosse, boxing, wrestling, basketball, hockey, archery, shooting, swimming, and baseball teams. He also made good use of his summers. Thorpe went 23–2 pitching minor-league baseball in 1910 and won gold medals in both the pentathlon and decathlon at the 1912 Olympics.

Gipp was a favorite of Knute Rockne. When "The Rock" took over the coaching reins at Notre Dame in 1918, his first move was to entrust the fate of his team to Gipp, who had impressed him in limited play the year before. Gipp was a tall, graceful athlete who excelled at every sport he tried. In fact, some claim he ranked among the best all-around athletes of his time. He loved to improvise, and at least once a game he tried something that no one had ever seen before. On offense, Gipp could elude tacklers or run right over them. He could throw with accuracy and kick the ball 50 yards in the air. On defense, he went three years without allowing his man to catch a pass. He was a masterful play-caller and a terrific leader. Toward the end of his senior season, Gipp developed a bad case of tonsillitis but insisted on playing against Northwestern in miserable weather. His condition worsened and he developed pneumonia. In those days, there was no medicine the doctors could give him, and he slipped away with Rockne at his side. Before Gipp died he told his coach that if Notre Dame was ever up against the wall in a game, he should tell his players to "win one for the Gipper." In 1928, Rockne found himself in just such a spot, when he brought one of his weakest teams to face undefeated Army. At halftime, instead of launching into his usual gung-ho pep talk, he calmly recounted this story to his players. They burst out of the locker room, tears streaming down their faces, and thrashed Army in the second half.

The Pros Pull Together

The pro game reverted back to small-time status when the Canton-Massillon rivalry—under a dark cloud of gambling-related suspicion—foundered after the 1906 season. Professional football did, however, stay alive, thanks to college stars who played under assumed names for a few bucks a game. The best teams sometimes drew more than a thousand fans, so there was enough money to hire a few good players, and by the mid-1910s pro ball was thriving again in such Ohio towns as Toledo, Youngstown, and Columbus. In Massillon, a new Tiger team was formed, and in 1915 the Canton Bulldogs pulled off a major coup by hiring Jim Thorpe for the princely sum of $250 a game.

Thorpe was down on his luck. When it was discovered he had pitched in the minor leagues during the summers of 1909 and 1910, he was stripped of his Olympic medals. He took a stab at major-league baseball, but had a hard time with training regulations and an even harder time hitting the curve. Considering Thorpe's talent and drawing power, $250 a game was hardly what he was worth—in his first appearance for Canton 8,000 fans showed up—but it was good money for playing the game he loved. Thorpe's presence also sparked a new rivalry between Canton and Massillon, and renewed enthusiasm for pro football. In 1916, many of the better teams in Ohio had at least one All-American in their lineup on a given Sunday, and another crazy salary spiral seemed just around the corner.

America's entry into World War I changed all that. Any able-bodied young man who was not in college was expected to join the military, leaving little for the pros in the way of raw material. It was one thing to sneak a few college boys into the lineup as high-priced ringers; it was another to field an entire team of college stars playing under assumed names. When the war ended, however, pro football picked up right where it had left off. Many college grads who had played football in the service sought employment in this growing field—so many in fact that several strong teams were formed from Pennsylvania all the way to Wisconsin.

In 1919, Canton added Thorpe's old Carlisle backfield mates, Joe Guyon and Pete Calac, and the team went undefeated. For the unofficial championship game against Massillon, the Bulldogs paid for the services of more than 40 players—mainly to keep them from playing for the Tigers! Thorpe was the hero, kicking a long field goal and punting the ball the length of the field when Massillon had Canton pinned against its own goal line late in the game.

One of the top teams in the country in 1919, the Hammond Pros, featured a well-known two-sport athlete named George Halas. He had starred both on the diamond and the gridiron for the University of Illinois and played big-league ball with the New York Yankees until a fellow named Babe Ruth came along and took his position. In 1920, Halas was hired by Staley Starchworks in Decatur, Illinois, to play for the company baseball team and coach its football team. The owner, A. E. Staley, believed that these teams were great advertisements for his company, and wanted Halas to put winners on the field. This he did, with the help of an attractive incentive package: Players would get a guaranteed year-round job, plus a share of gate receipts. They would also practice

The 1920 Decatur Staleys of the newly formed American Professional Football Association, the forerunner of the NFL.

two hours a day, on company time. The offer drew some of the top athletes in the Midwest, including former Notre Dame All-American center George Trafton and a number of men who had played alongside Halas at Illinois and on the Great Lakes Naval Station team during the war.

Halas then began the task of scheduling games for the Decatur Staleys. During this process, he discovered that a plan was in the works to form a professional league. Intrigued, he accepted the invitation of Bulldog manager Ralph Hay to meet with other interested parties at his Hupmobile auto dealership in Canton on August 20, 1920. Out of that meeting arose a loosely formed, 10-team circuit that included teams in Illinois, Ohio, and western New York. For its first two seasons it was called the American Professional Football Association (APFA). The teams agreed to respect each other's contracts so fans could get to know the same players week in and week out, and they also forbade the hiring of college players. Canton's Jim Thorpe was made honorary league president.

Despite a lot of confusion and a frightening number of empty seats, the league made it through its first season, albeit just barely. Every team lost money, but the players considered the APFA a resounding success—after all, they were making a living playing the game they loved. Among the stars during that first year was Fritz Pollard, a game-breaking runner who had earned All-America honors at Brown University. Pollard, an African-American, was the first of many black players to star in the league. Another was Paul Robeson, who played end for Akron while working his way through Columbia Law School. The league may have chosen the high road on the issue of

Legendary actor and singer Paul Robeson was also one of the first black players to compete in the APFA.

race (especially considering that blacks were banned altogether from organized baseball) but the players were a different story; when a black runner was tackled, he could count on getting worked over by his white peers. Thorpe was the league's big drawing card, although he concentrated mostly on coaching his Bulldogs. He was 33, had bad knees, and could no longer play an entire game. Most times he would wait until a crucial moment to insert himself. When he played, though, he was still spectacular.

The caliber of play in the league's first few seasons was good, but not really at the level of the best college teams of the day.

The players might have been a lot bigger and faster, but they played a more cautious game. Unlike college men, they did not practice on a daily basis, so the tricky running plays that were popular in college were harder to pull off. The lack of practice also made passing difficult. The big weapon in the league's early years was the punt. Most plays on first and second down were short running plays. On third down and long yardage, teams would typically send out one receiver and watch to see if he was covered. If he was open, the ball carrier would attempt a pass. If the defensive backs stayed close to the receiver, the back handling the football would have the option of booting a long kick down the field, hoping to pin his opponents deep in their own end. Games were won either by capitalizing on a mistake in enemy territory, blocking a punt and running it into the end zone, or by a magnificent run—either from scrimmage or on a punt or kickoff return.

In 1921, the APFA expanded to 21 teams, with the Green Bay Packers among the new entries. Thorpe was replaced as president by sports promoter Joe Carr. George Halas moved the Staleys to Chicago after his employer decided to drop the company-sponsored football team. The following season, he renamed his club the Bears. Thanks to Halas, the league got a new name, too: the National Football League. Over the next few seasons, the infant NFL stumbled along, feeling its way as a sideshow to the booming college game.

College Football 1921–33

The 1920s saw college football achieve a social status that would have been unimag-inable just a decade earlier. The country's economy was booming, people were spending up to a quarter of their income on leisure activities, and millions of people were obsessed with sports. Television had yet to arrive and radio offerings were few, so people attended events in person. Universities that had once struggled to draw a few thousand spectators to their games now found themselves trying to accommodate tens of thousands. Football programs were generating millions of dollars for schools, and schools poured tremendous resources into hiring the best coaches, building the most modern stadiums, and attracting the top players. The nation's network of roads and railways was vastly improved during World War I, making it much easier for a college team to play out of its region; the news media now had the technology to carry news and photos from games all over the country. In many ways, college football was becoming more of a national sport than the national pastime itself. Indeed, it would be nearly four decades before major league baseball went "coast to coast." Fueling the college-football boom were the sport's star players, and the two most celebrated grid-iron figures during the 1920s were Knute Rockne and Red Grange.

Rockne coached Notre Dame, the dominant team of the era. In 13 seasons between 1918 and 1930 his teams won 105 games, tied 5, and lost just 12. The Notre Dame coach did more than anyone to promote college ball as a national sport. He scheduled games in the east and the west, against the best teams, and in the biggest cities. He brought the excitement and pageantry of the big event to millions. And, most important, he won. Rockne's coaching ability was the stuff of legend. He knew how to analyze an

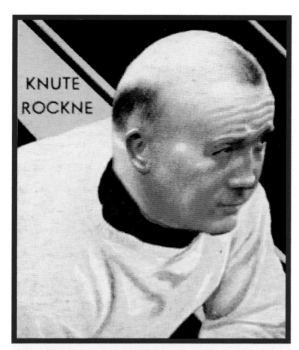

KNUTE
ROCKNE

The name Knute Rockne became synonymous with winning during the 1920s. The innovative and inspirational Notre Dame coach made sure his teams got exposure in every part of the country, helping to bring national popularity to college football.

opponent and find a way to beat them. This might mean drawing up a new group of plays, or working out a new game plan. Often, the answer was just getting his players to want the win more than the other team. In this regard, he might have been the best motivator ever.

As Notre Dame's fame increased, the school attracted better players. Rockne took advantage of all the talent with a system he called "smart football," which relied less on brute force and more on creative play-calling. He tinkered with the standard T-formation, adding complex blocking schemes that greatly increased a signal-caller's options in

the huddle. Fans at Notre Dame games were getting a glimpse of a brand of football that was still about 15 or 20 years away. As Rockne bent the rules and went against many of football's most sacred conventions, fans also saw such hallmarks of modern football as platooning and specialization.

The height of Notre Dame's reign came between 1922 and 1924, when a quartet of marvelous two-way players blossomed together. Elmer Layden, Jim Crowley, Don Miller, and Harry Stuhlreder rushed for more than 5,000 yards during those three seasons, and Notre Dame lost only two games. In 1924, the team went undefeated and won the national championship. Layden, Crowley, and Stuhlreder were each unanimous choices for All-America honors, while Miller led the team with 763 rushing yards. So dominant were these players that sportswriter Grantland Rice, borrowing from the Bible's Book of Revelations, dubbed them "the Four Horsemen"—the righteous bringers of God's apocalyptic wrath. When a photo of the quartet mounted on horseback hit the country's newspapers, they became national celebrities.

When other colleges saw the publicity Notre Dame was getting—and how that translated into enormous gate receipts—a mad scramble ensued as they pursued the best players. And they tried even harder to come up with heroic nicknames for their stars. The University of Illinois, however, already had the top college player, with an unbeatable nickname—Red Grange, "the Galloping Ghost." He had earned this moniker the year before, when he led Illinois to the national championship. When Grange got a running start, he could run into a pile of tacklers, disappear for a moment, and then somehow reappear on the other

Notre Dame's famed "Four Horsemen" in the saddle; from left, Elmer Layden, Jim Crowley, Don Miller, and Harry Stuhlreder.

side. This skill—in reality a combination of speed, power, great moves, and impeccable instincts—was unheard of in football, and it absolutely electrified the crowds. Every time Grange touched the ball, tens of thousands of fans would leap to their feet and start cheering wildly. He was the kind of player you never took your eyes off, because at any moment he might do something you would remember for a lifetime.

At about the same time the Four Horsemen were making headlines, Grange, a junior, scored four touchdowns in the first quarter of a meeting with a Michigan team that had not lost in 20 games. He did this on runs of 95, 67, 56, and 45 yards. Later in the game, he ran for a fifth touchdown and passed for a sixth. The following season, a so-so Illinois squad traveled to the University of Pennsylvania and upset the Quakers 24-2, with Grange amassing 363 total yards and scoring all three of his team's touch-

downs. After the game, he was proclaimed the finest football player in the land.

Among the other top stars of the 1920s were Ernie Nevers and Bronko Nagurski. Nevers played for coach Pop Warner, whose fame at the Carlisle Indian School had won him a plum job at Stanford University. There Nevers handled the ball on almost every play, and in his junior year he led the team to the 1925 Rose Bowl against Notre Dame despite fracturing both ankles over the course of the season. Against Rockne's Four Horsemen, he played all 60 minutes, gained 114 yards, and was in on more than half of Stanford's tackles. Stanford lost, but Nevers was a big winner, grabbing the football world's attention at the start of the next season and never letting it go. Stanford lost but one game in 1925 and Nevers was an easy choice for All-America honors. As for Bronko Nagurski, the 6'2", 225-pound University of Minnesota fullback was as big

THE ROSE BOWL

In 1902, officials for the annual Tournament of Roses in Pasadena, California, decided to stage a sporting event as part of the festivities. They arranged a game between Stanford University and the University of Michigan. Stanford was humiliated 49-0 and tournament officials decided to replace the football game with something a little more interesting: chariot races. By 1916, the public clamored for another stab at football and the Tournament of Roses obliged, scheduling an exhibition between Washington State University and Brown University. This time the west coast team scored the shutout, 14-0, and the game has been played every year since. Rechristened the Rose Bowl in 1923, the game generally matched the best team in the west against one of the top teams east of the Mississippi. Considered the granddaddy of all bowl games, the Rose Bowl remains college football's most anticipated annual sporting event.

as most linemen of his day. A devastating blocker, he was actually more valuable barreling over opponents than carrying the football. Indeed, he played 12 of his 22 college games at the tackle position. When he did get the ball, though, it was every man for himself. On defense, he was an All-America lineman.

Tragedy struck the college-football world in 1931 when Notre Dame coach Knute Rockne perished in a plane crash. Rockne's influence, however, lasted for many years afterward. When he died, 23 of his former players were head coaches for other colleges, and more than 150 were teaching his theories at the high-school level.

Pro Football 1920–32

The NFL watched as all these fresh-faced college men made national headlines, and wondered what it had to do to attract even a fraction of that attention. Part of the problem was in play-for-pay itself—football fans in the 1920s found the college stars attractive because they were well-educated amateurs, unsullied by the dubious professional game. They saw the NFL as somehow beneath their heroes, and they had little interest in following the progress of a player once he had left the college ranks. What pro football needed was someone so magnetic that he would literally pull fans into the stadiums.

Thanks largely to the myth-makers who wrote the country's sports columns, the league got their man in the person of Red Grange. After his incredible 1925 season for Illinois, Grange turned pro immediately and signed with the Chicago Bears. He hired an agent, C. C. Pyle, who specialized in creating huge events, and hammered out a deal that gave him a big salary and a healthy cut of the gate receipts. The agree-

Red Grange of the New York Football Yankees breaks free for a big gain in a 1926 game.

ment would make Grange the highest-paid athlete in sports.

Grange had to work hard for his money. Less than a week after his final college game he was playing for the Bears in a 0-0 Thanksgiving Day tie with the Chicago Cardinals. Although Grange was held to just a few yards on the ground, he ignited the crowd with some thrilling punt returns and saved the day with a goal-line interception. Five days later, not even a snowstorm could keep 28,000 fans from coming to see Grange lead the Bears to a 14-13 win over the Columbus Tigers. Then the schedule got really tough. From December 2 to December 13, Grange and the Bears played eight games, taking on teams in St. Louis; Philadelphia; New York; Washington, D.C.; Boston; Pittsburgh; and Detroit before finally finishing up in Chicago. Sixty-five

thousand New Yorkers came to the Polo Grounds to see Grange and the Bears play the hometown Giants, pulling the New York franchise out of deep debt. The Bears split their eight games, and Grange suffered an arm injury that kept him out of the final two contests.

Undaunted, Pyle and Halas scheduled a second tour, which began on Christmas Day. This road trip lasted through January and included games in nine warm-weather cities in Florida, Louisiana, California, Oregon, and Washington. The Bears won eight and lost one, playing mostly against all-star squads made up of pros and collegians. The highlights of the tour included the professional debut of Ernie Nevers, as well as several dramatic head-to-head battles with Washington All-American Wildcat Wilson. Jim Thorpe also appeared in one game, for the Tampa Cardinals, but at the age of 37 he had little left. The game in Los Angeles drew 75,000 fans, which set a pro attendance record. In all, more than 300,000 fans saw the Galloping Ghost play in a span of less than 10 weeks. The tour made Grange a wealthy man, catapulted Pyle to the top of the sports-marketing business, and established Halas as the NFL's most influential owner. It also gave the professional game the legitimacy it so desperately needed. Pro football finally had a national star who was already a household name. The NFL had captured a little bit of the sporting spotlight.

Lost in the mists of time is the fact that Grange was a wonderful defensive back. He won as many games with crucial tackles and clutch interceptions as he did with spine-tingling touchdown runs. This was typical of the pro game in the 1920s, which placed a premium on versatility. Substitutions were strictly limited, and payrolls were too small to carry any "specialists." To make it in the NFL a player had to have skill both on offense and defense. Toughness and durability were highly prized, too.

Among the great two-way players of the NFL's first decade were Curly Lambeau and Guy Chamberlain. Chamberlain was nicknamed "The Champ," and for good reason: in five of the six years he played in the pros, his team won the league title. A talented end in the days when receiving skills were still being invented game to game, he broke in with Jim Thorpe's Canton Bulldogs in 1919 and helped the team to an undefeated season. In 1920 and 1921, he played with the Decatur Staleys, who went 21–2–2 over that span, and it was Chamberlain's 70-yard interception return for a touchdown that provided the winning margin against Buffalo in the 1921 Championship Game. He returned

to Canton as a player-coach, and led the team to a pair of undefeated seasons and NFL titles in 1922 and 1923. In 1925, the franchise shifted to Cleveland, and Chamberlain again took his team to the league championship!

Lambeau was another successful player-coach during the 1920s. Although he won fewer championships than Chamberlain, his place in history is much more significant. After leaving Notre Dame because of tonsillitis, he took a job as a clerk with the Indian Packing Company in his Wisconsin hometown of Green Bay. In the winter of 1919, Lambeau convinced his boss that there were enough good players in the factory to field a semipro football team, and the Green Bay Packers were born. The team became a member of the APFA in 1921, and over the next decade—with the financial help of Green Bay's fans and business community—the Packers held their own while franchises in bigger NFL cities failed one after the other. A daring passer and relentless ball carrier, Lambeau remained one of the top players in the league until he retired in 1929.

College Football 1934–41

Despite dwindling attendance and financial difficulties, college football continued to grow during the Great Depression. The game itself continued to evolve. Agreeing with the pros that more passing would make for more excitement, the colleges followed the NFL's lead and adopted a new ball for the 1934 season. Yet while many teams used the pass to open up their games, the running game attained a balletlike precision. Backs popped up and shifted around, linemen

BENNY FRIEDMAN: THE NFL'S FIRST DEADLY PASSER

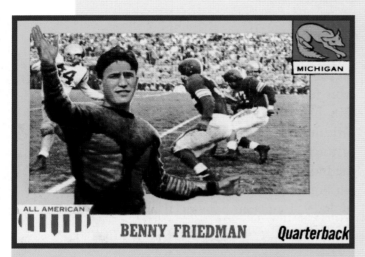

MICHIGAN

ALL AMERICAN

BENNY FRIEDMAN *Quarterback*

Benny Friedman, who shook up defenses with his throwing ability first at the University of Michigan and later in the NFL.

Red Grange's contribution to the growth of pro football is unquestionable. But another star of the 1920s, Benny Friedman, had a far greater impact in terms of the how the game would one day be played. Friedman believed that the key to winning in football was to open up the field through the development of a passing attack. He spent years stretching his fingers so that he could grip the melon-shaped ball used in the 1920s, and lifted weights to develop his forearms and shoulders. By the time he graduated from the University of Michigan he could throw accurate spirals. Friedman broke in with the Cleveland Bulldogs in 1927, then moved to the Detroit Wolverines in 1928 after Cleveland folded. The second-year tailback led the NFL in passing and scoring, and was among the leading rushers. In 1929, Giants owner Tim Mara purchased the Wolverines, folded the franchise, and kept Friedman. His hope was that his new quarter

twirled around each other to execute stunning blocks, and there was an element of razzle-dazzle that made fans feel like something incredible could happen on any given play.

The media had a lot to do with the game's increasing popularity. Radio now enabled fans to listen to games they could not attend. Lavish preseason guides and magazines carrying rosters, player photos, analyses, and predictions allowed fans in every part of the country to access information that had not been previously available; they could now match the names of the country's top stars with faces and biograph-

ical information. And in 1936 the Associated Press (AP) wire service began publishing national rankings each week. Fans could not wait to open the newspaper to see who had climbed and who had fallen after each slate of Saturday games.

The 1930s also saw the spread of college bowl games beyond California. In 1935, the first Orange Bowl was held in Miami and the first Sugar Bowl was held in New Orleans. In 1936, the first Sun Bowl was held in El Paso, Texas, and in 1937 the first Cotton Bowl was held in the city of Dallas. These games were an outgrowth of the popular postseason charity contests held

back would continue to put up big numbers and—because he was Jewish—attract thousands of new fans to the game.

Friedman threw for a record-shattering 20 touchdowns and tossed four in one game. The Giants were coming off a disastrous year, during which they won just four games and lost a reported $40,000. Friedman led the team to 12 wins in 1929, attracted thousands of new fans, and put the Giants in the black for the first time. In 1930, he enjoyed another exceptional season, and the Giants made money again.

Friedman did not throw a lot of passes by modern standards—usually just a dozen a game—but he would throw on any down, and from any place on the field. In Friedman's case, the threat of the pass was just as effective as the pass itself. When he took a handoff or pitchout, defenders backpedaled instead of rushing up to meet him. This gave him an extra second to decide whether to pass, run, or lateral to a teammate.

Friedman left football briefly in 1931 to pursue business opportunities, but returned midway through the schedule when those opportunities failed to materialize. After the season he asked for a share of the Giants. When his request was turned down, he decided to sign with the Bears, but his wife refused to leave New York. Eventually, he settled on a player-coach arrangement with the NFL's Brooklyn team. He retired for good at 29.

Friedman had convinced NFL owners that a wide-open passing attack was the key to increasing attendance. Prior to the 1933 season, they voted to change the shape of the ball, making it more aerodynamic. They also instituted other rules to swing the balance of power toward the offense.

earlier in the decade. The bowl games themselves were generally part of a bigger civic celebration or festival, and although they were considered exhibition games at first, eventually they figured very heavily in determining the national championship.

The prewar era also saw the first major influx of national stars from the south. Three of the college game's top receivers—Don Hutson, Jerry Dalrymple, and Gaynell Tinsley—were all from southern schools, as were passing sensation Sammy Baugh and big-play specialist Bobby Wilson. Many of the top linemen also played their ball in the south, including Bob Suffridge, Ki Aldrich,

Fred Crawford, and Bruiser Kinard. The names most familiar to fans of the day, however, were not from southern schools.

Byron "Whizzer" White played for the University of Colorado, and led the nation in scoring in 1937 with 122 points. That same year he had the unusual distinction of producing both the longest punt (84 yards) as well as the longest punt return (97 yards). White was slippery going through the line and flat-out fast in the open field, and he was an exceptional pass-coverage man on defense. He also happened to be the most well-rounded student-athlete in America. He started for the baseball team, was an

FIFTEEN CENTS October 25, 1937

TIME

The Weekly Newsmagazine

Color Photograph for Time by Leigh Irwin & Nicholas Lampos

Volume XXX

DUKE'S WADE
Southward the source of football takes its way.
(See Sport)

Number 17

As this cover from *Time* magazine testifies, college football had become national news in the 1930s; furthermore, southern colleges were beginning to produce powerful teams and some of the country's best players.

All-Conference basketball star, and earned a Rhodes scholarship to study at Oxford University in England. After finishing at Colorado, he played three years in the NFL (and led the league in rushing twice), graduated first in his class at Yale Law School, and served as a Naval intelligence officer during World War II. It was in the Navy that he met and befriended John Kennedy, who was elected president of the United States in 1960. Two years later, Kennedy appointed White to the U.S. Supreme Court.

Tom Harmon of the University of Michigan Wolverines did not have White's resume, but he could lay claim to being the last great "triple threat" tailback. He was a smooth and powerful runner, a superb passer, and he had a strong, accurate right leg. A two-time All-American, he won the Heisman Trophy in 1940 and was named the AP's Athlete of the Year. In a 41-0 romp against the University of California, Harmon scored on runs of 72, 80, 86, and 94 yards. He scored 237 points in three varsity seasons and threw 16 TD passes.

YOU'RE THE TOPS

In 1935, New York's Downtown Athletic Club decided to recognize the top player east of the Mississippi River with a special trophy. Jay Berwanger of the University of Chicago was selected, beating out Monk Meyer of Army, Bill Shakespeare of Notre Dame, and Pepper Constable of Princeton. In 1936, voting was expanded to encompass all schools across the country and the award was named the Heisman Memorial Trophy in honor of John Heisman, the club's athletic director and a legendary college coach. Over the years it has come to be regarded as the "most valuable player" award of college football, although charges have been leveled from time to time that it is more of a popularity contest.

Nile Kinnick of the University of Iowa had a year to remember in 1939, when he led the lightly regarded Hawkeyes to a 6–1–1 record. Guiding the team's offense from the quarterback position, he spurred Iowa to one amazing come-from-behind win after another against big-time opponents. Against Indiana University Kinnick lined up for the game-tying field goal, then rifled a pass to a streaking receiver for the winning score. Against unbeaten Notre Dame, he kept the Irish pinned deep in their own territory with 16 long punts, then scored a TD and kicked the point-after for a 7-6 victory. Against powerful Minnesota, Kinnick erased a 9-0 fourth-quarter deficit with a pair of long touchdown passes that brought the Hawkeyes their best win of the season. For good measure, he also picked off eight passes on defense! Needless to say, he won the Heisman Trophy. Kinnick enlisted in the Navy during World War II and became a fighter pilot. He was killed in the spring of 1943 when his engine failed over the Caribbean.

Kinnick was one of the first players to draw attention to the quarterback position, which was slowly gaining in stature. The quarterback's job had always been to take the snap and then get the ball to his more talented teammates. Now coaches were beginning to see the sense in putting their best athlete at that position, especially if he could pass.

The most successful program of the pre–World War II era belonged to the University of Minnesota, a team that relied on smothering an opponent's game. From 1933 to 1941, the Golden Gophers went 58–9–5 and recorded shutouts in nearly half of their victories. Coach Bernie Bierman drilled his players relentlessly until they could recog-

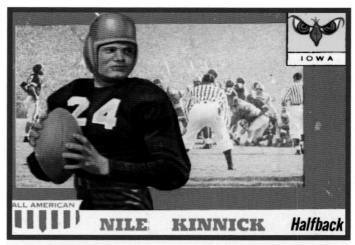

Quarterback Nile Kinnick had a spectacular season in 1939 for the University of Iowa and won the Heisman Trophy.

nize and destroy virtually anything their Big Ten opponents threw at them. His approach to offense was to concentrate on running a small group of plays and throwing blocks that could be heard in every corner of the stadium. In 1934, the team went 8–0 and won the national championship. Of the 11 players on the All-America team that year, 3—halfback Pug Lund, end Butch Larson, and guard Bill Bevan—played for Bierman.

Bierman's teams continued to dominate, sharing the national title with Southern Methodist University in 1935 and winning it outright in 1936, 1940, and 1941. Among the standouts who made those teams next-to-unbeatable were linemen Ed Widseth and Urban Odson, halfback George Franck, end Ray King, and the star of the 1940 and 1941 teams, Bruce Smith. Smith was the Big Ten's most exciting runner, longest kicker, and best passer—a "dream back" if there ever was one. His spectacular 80-yard run on a muddy field in 1940 sunk Michigan 7-6 and nailed down the national title. In

1941, Smith was hobbled by a bad knee, but still managed to guide the Golden Gophers to an undefeated season. For his fine performance, he won the Heisman Trophy. He even got to play himself in the 1942 film *Smith of Minnesota*.

Pro Football 1933–45

If the years 1895–1919 represented the infancy of professional football, and the years 1920–32 had been its childhood, then the pre–World War II era was its adolescence. The game was getting a lot smarter, but it was still feeling its way, a bit clumsy at times. Offenses were as concerned with keeping the ball in the center of the field as they were gaining yardage. Consequently, defenses bunched toward the middle, almost daring opponents to run toward the sidelines. This got to be pretty tiresome, both to the players and the fans. The owners agreed. The Great Depression had hit the game hard, and crowds were dwindling. Big names were no longer enough to keep the turnstiles clicking—the game itself had to be more exciting.

Prior to the 1933 season, Bears owner George Halas and Redskins owner George Preston Marshall pushed through several new rules. Players no longer had to throw a forward pass from five yards behind the line of scrimmage; they could now throw from any point behind the line. Two sets of hashmarks—each 30 feet in from the sidelines— were added to the field, along with a rule that brought the ball back to the hashmarks after plays that ended near the sidelines or out of bounds. The goal posts, which had been moved back in 1927, were returned to the goal line. And the ball itself, which for so long had been shaped to favor the kick-

ing part of football, was streamlined to make it easier to pass and carry.

These changes had their intended effects. Wiping out the five-yard no-pass rule meant that a team could throw quick passes right after the ball was snapped, or send a passer scrambling down the line of scrimmage waiting for a receiver to get open. It also enabled teams to display more finesse and engage in more deception, as multiple fakes and handoffs were now possible. The hashmark rule opened the game up even more. Teams no longer had to waste a down trying to get back to the middle of the field when tackled near the sideline—they could use that down to advance the football. Consequently, for the first time ever offenses could treat the sideline as an area of opportunity rather than one of danger, which further spread the defense. Finally, the new location of the goal posts touched off an explosion in field goals, at least by the standards of the day. In the 1920s, a team would have been lucky to make more than one field goal a year; after the goal posts were brought forward, most teams attempted at least one a game. Although scoring did not rise dramatically there were fewer tie games—a team needed only to get within its kicker's range during the final seconds to have a shot at winning it.

Another important change to the pro game for 1933 was the creation of Eastern and Western divisions and the establishment of a championship game pitting the division champs against each other. This kept fan interest high through the season, and kept the pro game in the newspapers well into the fall. The NFL still lagged far behind college football—both in fan interest and media coverage—but it was making slow, steady gains. Pro football during the Great Depression was still primarily a running game, but it was far more imaginative and daring than it had been during the 1920s. Teams often had three men in the backfield who could both run and pass, and employed fakes and trick plays after the ball was snapped. Teams now featured several set passing plays, whereas in the past they would put the ball in the air only as a last option.

One great NFL passer emerged during the prewar years: Sammy Baugh. He was an incredible all-around athlete who in many ways changed the way football was played at the professional level. After he came to the Redskins in 1937, he played seven seasons at the tailback position in Washington's single-wing formation, and he led the league in passing three times. He riddled enemy defenses with passes that ranged from short pops to long bombs. Despite a weird grip, he could drill the football through the tightest opening, or float it into the hands of a sprinting receiver. Baugh was, for all practical purposes, football's first modern passer. Ironically, it was not until the Redskins revamped their offense in 1944 that he actually played quarterback. Yet by the time Baugh retired after the 1952 season he not only held every major passing record, but he had also established the quarterback position as the most influential in football.

While Baugh was making news throwing the ball, Don Hutson of the Green Bay Packers was garnering headlines by catching it. He transformed the pass from something of a novelty item into the game's most explosive offensive weapon. He was so much better than anyone else in his era that most football experts credit him with inventing the wide-receiver position. Indeed, Hutson was playing 1990s-style foot-

Slingin' Sammy Baugh of the Washington Redskins drills the ball downfield to a receiver. Baugh riddled defenses with short passes and the occasional long bomb, and was football's first modern passer.

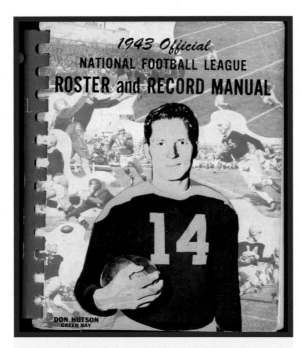

Green Bay Packers receiver Don Hutson graces the cover of this 1943 NFL yearbook. Hutson had great speed, hands, and leaping ability, but it was his intelligence and precise route-running that made him the father of the wide-receiver position.

ball against defenders who were still coming to terms with the changes of the 1930s. He had enormous, soft hands, great leaping ability, and flawless concentration. He made precise cuts and could generate a burst of extra speed just as the ball was coming down. The only option defenses had was to put one defensive back on him tight, and keep another in reserve for when Hutson shook the first man. Even so, he caught 99 touchdown passes in his 11-year career—a mark it took Jerry Rice eight 16-game seasons to surpass. A fine defensive player, Hutson specialized in—what else?—interceptions.

The most feared runner of the prewar era was Bronko Nagurski of the Chicago Bears, who became a much better player than he had been in college. He was the NFL's first true power back. There was nothing fancy about what Nagurski did, but short of piling three or four men on top of him, no one ever found a consistent way to neutralize him. Nagurski posed a special problem for the defenses of the day. He was as big as the best linemen yet he was very fast, and once he got going he was very difficult to stop. Making matters worse, every so often Nagurski would straighten up and whip a perfect pass, so swarming him with tacklers could have disastrous consequences. Opponents literally bounced off of him, and he often dragged two men several yards before a third joined in to finish him off. Nagurski's strength was the stuff of legend—people liked to say that he was the only back who ran his own interference, or that the only way to stop him was to shoot him in the locker room. On defense, Nagurski played with such ferocity that teams routinely assigned two blockers to him on almost every play. In his fifth NFL season, he was joined in the backfield by Beattie Feathers, an All-American tailback out of the University of Tennessee. Although Nagurski still did the bulk of Chicago's running, Feathers got the ball 101 times and—running behind Nagurski's bone-crushing blocks—averaged 9.9 yards a carry, led the league in touchdowns, and became the first player in history to gain more than 1,000 yards. Anyone who knew anything about football knew that two-thirds of those numbers belonged to the Bronk.

The evolution of professional football reached its highest level during the prewar era neither in Don Hutson's Packers nor in

Brawny Bronko Nagurski, one of the most punishing runners in NFL history, definitely did not wear a smile when he rumbled toward defenders during a real game.

Sammy Baugh's Redskins, but in the multi-talented Chicago Bears. Gone by this time were the old rough-and-tumble stars of the early 1930s. They had been replaced by young guns such as razor-sharp quarterback Sid Luckman and bruising fullback Bill Os-manski. In 1940 the team harvested one of the greatest rookie crops in history, adding lineman Bulldog Turner, breakaway runner

George McAfee, and end Ken Kavanagh to an already strong team. Coach George Halas revived the old T-formation and inserted the strong-armed Luckman at quarterback, and the results were magical. The Bears went to the championship game four years in a row from 1940 to 1943, winning three times. In the 1940 title game, the team recorded the most significant and lopsided blowout in NFL history, beating the Redskins 73-0. So well-developed was the Chicago system that even when the team lost its best players to the military when war came, the second stringers continued to dominate the league for two more seasons.

College Football 1942–59

The college game flourished during World War II, despite a shortage of manpower and severe travel restrictions. Not surprisingly, the United States Military Academy had a

The 1940 Chicago Bears had reason to hoist coach George Halas after they stomped Washington 73-0 in the NFL championship game.

THE NFL DURING WARTIME

World War II had a devastating effect on the NFL. Whereas major-league baseball was able to limp along with old and injured players, this option did not really suit pro football. It was hard enough for a young, healthy player to make it through a season; it would prove virtually impossible for players who were not 100 percent. The other thing going against football during the war was that college ball was no longer sending its stars to the NFL. The league had come to rely on the publicity generated by big-name college players who turned pro; now they were enlisting in the military. In all, more than 600 NFL players, coaches, and front-office people went to war, and 20 never came back. All-NFL tackle Al Blozis of the Giants was the most notable player killed.

The league considered suspending operations after the military draft decimated its rosters in 1942. Instead, some drastic changes were made. The Cleveland Rams were dropped temporarily for the 1943 season, the Steelers merged rosters with the Eagles in 1943, then did the same with the Chicago Cardinals in 1944. A new team, the Boston Yanks, entered the league in 1944, but in 1945, the Brooklyn Dodgers—never a stable franchise—went belly-up. The NFL made it through World War II by the skin of its teeth, but it emerged a leaner, more confident organization. That was important, for although the war had nearly destroyed pro football, it would turn out to be the catalyst for an era of explosive growth.

great team during these years. While other schools lost promising recruits to the military, Army *was* the military—each student was there to learn how to become an officer. If they happened to be great football players, that was okay with Army. From 1944 to 1946, the Cadets had one of the legendary one-two punches in football history, with fullback Doc Blanchard and halfback Glenn Davis. Behind a massive offensive line, the two stars ran roughshod over the competition, leading Army to a pair of perfect seasons and national championships, and then a 9–0–1 record during their final year together.

Coach Earl "Red" Blaik used these two runners to perfection. Blanchard, a big, bruising runner, plowed through the middle for big yards, averaging 7.1 per carry in 1945, when he won the Heisman Trophy. His nickname was "Mr. Inside." Davis, who was nicknamed "Mr. Outside," generally took the ball around end, either behind the blocking of Blanchard or after a Blanchard fake into the line. Davis averaged over 11 yards per carry in 1944 and 1945, finishing second in the Heisman voting both years. In 1946, he won the Heisman, despite averaging far fewer yards. Davis was particularly good around the goal line, and both players

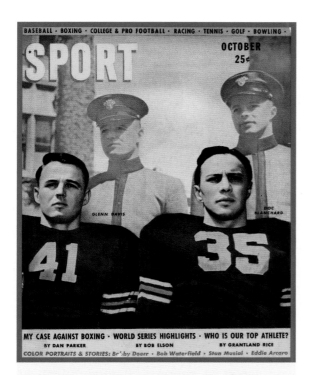

With the nation at war in the 1940s, Army had no trouble fielding blue-chip recruits. The best were fullback Doc Blanchard and halfback Glenn Davis, who together led Army to two national championships.

were excellent defenders, picking off a combined 21 passes during their careers.

When World War II ended, it appeared as if Notre Dame was on the verge of building a college football dynasty again. National champions in 1943, the school achieved Top Ten rankings throughout the war and reclaimed the top spot in the polls in 1946, 1947, and 1949. The coach who brought the Fighting Irish back to national prominence was Frank Leahy. He did not cut the dramatic figure Knute Rockne had, but he was every bit as dedicated to teaching his players how to win. And win they did. During those four magnificent seasons they were tied twice and never beaten.

The Fighting Irish were led by Johnny Lujack, George Connor, and Leon Hart. Lujack was the team's quarterback when they won the national championship in 1943. He went to war for two years, then returned to pick up right where he had left off, leading the team to an 8–0–1 record and the national title in 1946. His game-saving open-field tackle of Doc Blanchard preserved a scoreless tie against Army, without which the Irish would have fallen short of the national championship. In 1947, Lujack won the Heisman Trophy and was named the AP's Athlete of the Year. After he graduated, the Notre Dame backfield kept right on rolling with two All-America replacements, Emil Sitko and Bob Williams.

Connor was the defensive star of the 1946 and 1947 teams, winning the Outland Trophy as the nation's top lineman as a junior. He was quick, strong, and tenacious enough to shed blocker after blocker until he found the ball carrier. If a team ran past him or away from him, he had the raw speed to catch up to a play and save a touchdown. Hart, who stood 6'5" and weighed 260 pounds, was a blocking end on those two teams. In 1948 and 1949, Leahy worked him more into the offense, throwing him the ball and even using him as a fullback on short-yardage downs. So great an influence was Hart in the games he played that, though he didn't put up eye-popping numbers, he was awarded the Heisman Trophy in 1949.

As the 1950s began, it was not the Irish who had the team to beat, but the University of Oklahoma. The 35-year-old coach of the Sooners, Bud Wilkinson, had learned a formation called the "Split T" from its creator while in the service. He added some wrinkles of his own when he became Okla-

Oklahoma had the top college program of the 1950s. Here Sooners coach Bud Wilkinson poses before a practice with quarterback Gene Calame (right) and center Gene Mears.

homa's top man in 1947, creating a blocking scheme that allowed his ball carrier to angle toward the line and choose the best-looking hole to run through. It was simple to explain but extremely difficult to stop. Between 1948 and 1950, Wilkinson's Sooners won 31 games in a row, and he was named Coach of the Year in 1949. From 1953 to 1957, the team reeled off 47 consecutive victories. Oklahoma went unbeaten in 1950, 1955, and 1956, winning the national championship each year.

Critical to the Sooner machine were its linemen, including end Max Boydston, tackle Jim Weatherall, guards J. D. Roberts, Bo Bollinger, and Bill Crisher, and centers Kurt Burris and Jerry Tubbs. Running behind these All-Americans were several talented running backs, including Leon Heath, Billy Vessels, and Tommy McDonald. Nicknamed "Mule Train" for the way he dragged opposing tacklers, Heath was a big fullback who led the nation with 9.1 yards per carry in 1949. Heath was the team's only returning starter in 1950, yet he managed to lead Oklahoma to the national championship. In 1952, Vessels ran for more than 1,000 yards and scored 18 touchdowns to win the Heisman Trophy. He excelled in every phase of the game, both on offense and defense. He was as cagey a runner as there was, picking his spots beautifully in Wilkinson's system.

The best player to star for Wilkinson's great teams was McDonald. In his three varsity seasons the Sooners never lost. And during his two years as a starter Oklahoma won a pair of national championships. At 5'9" McDonald was small even by 1950s standards, but he specialized in making big plays. He averaged around seven yards per carry, as the Oklahoma offense offered all sorts of holes for the speedy halfback to shoot through. Although rarely called upon to catch the ball, he could do so as well as anyone in the country. McDonald knew how to get into the end zone, and he knew how to keep other teams out. On both sides of the ball, he was a true gamer.

Jim Brown of Syracuse was probably the scariest player of the 1950s. At any given time he was likely to be the strongest player on the field, as well as the fastest. As a senior in 1956 he led the Orangemen to a 7–1 record, and paced the nation with 6.2 yards per carry. Brown did everything, including kicking extra points and playing a pretty mean linebacker. It was as a ball carrier, however, that he truly excelled. Brown knew that most players went limp when they were tackled in order to avoid injury

A KNACK FOR THE SPECTACULAR

One of the most intriguing players of the era was Pete Dawkins of Army. Dawkins had a good year in 1957, gaining 665 yards and leading Army back into the Top Twenty with an 8–2 record. He carried the ball for just 428 yards in 1958 and grabbed just 16 passes, but it was one of those crazy, incredible years. Every time Dawkins touched the ball, something spectacular happened. He ran for 12 touchdowns, and of the 16 balls he caught he ran in 6 for scores. These were not short passes, but long, spectacular runs. Indeed, Dawkins led the nation that year in yards per catch with a mark of 30.9. He also won the Heisman Trophy, and Army finished with an 8–0–1 record and a number-three national ranking. After graduation, Dawkins received a Rhodes scholarship and went to study at Oxford, where he became a rugby star. When he returned to the United States he went into the military and in 1983 became the army's youngest general at 45. After he retired, he became a U.S. Senator.

when they hit the ground. He also knew that tacklers loosened their grip just a bit when they felt their victim giving up. Brown perfected the subtle skill of going limp just for an instant, then exploding out of the tackle for a few more yards. When defensive players figured this out, they would spend the rest of the game squeezing him as hard as they could until his knees hit the ground. But the joke was on them—by the end of a game they were so exhausted from this extra effort that he could roll right over them.

The Pro Game Flourishes

In 1946, players returning from the military joined the top college graduates to produce an unprecedented glut of football talent for the pros. With the economy booming and people willing and able to concentrate on sports again, pro football seemed like a no-lose proposition. Eight wealthy investors agreed, and put up the money for the charter franchises in the All-American Football Conference. The AAFC went head-to-head with the NFL, signing dozens of top players away from league rosters, landing several top college stars, and driving up salaries for all pro players. The AAFC put two teams on the west coast—the Los Angeles Dons and the San Francisco 49ers—and one in Miami, marking the first time major-league sports franchises had ever come to these areas. Not to be outdone, the NFL moved its 1945 champion, the Cleveland Rams, to Los Angeles.

The game's bloated payrolls kept most teams from turning a profit, even though attendance was strong for both leagues. By the end of the 1940s, however, the postwar economy was starting to level off, fans grew tired of following so many pro-football teams, and attendance began to drop, espe-

THE STRUGGLE TO INTEGRATE THE NFL

During the 1920s and early 1930s, football was the only professional sport in which fans could see black athletes and white athletes on the same team. Many black players who had starred for college teams in the 1910s and 1920s went on to play football professionally—some in semipro and sandlot leagues, others for barnstorming teams, and a total of 16 in the NFL. This did not mean they were welcome. On the contrary, when a black player got his hands on the ball a cry of "Get that nigger!" usually followed. Fritz Pollard, one of the best players in the early days of the NFL, used to roll on his back and stick his cleats in the air after being tackled to discourage white players from piling on top of him. Duke Slater of the Rock Island Independents had to sit out a game against the Kansas City Blues because they refused to play against a black man. The Blues scored an upset that day, costing the Independents a shot at the NFL title. Slater put up with these indignities for 10 years, and still established himself as one of the greatest tackles ever to play.

By 1934, there were no longer any black players on NFL rosters. It is not clear why this happened, but it was probably a decision made by the owners. At the height of the Great Depression, they must have feared that giving even a single job to a black man would have alienated countless white fans.

Given that baseball was holding the "color line," there was little or no pressure to reintegrate the NFL. In 1939, the Chicago Bears played a team of black all-stars and killed them 51-0. This all but guaranteed that no black player would be signed by an NFL team, although George Halas toyed with the idea of signing UCLA tailback Kenny Washington in 1940. Washington teamed with Jackie Robinson in the Bruin backfield, and these two formed a lethal trio with end Woody Strode.

Ironically, it was Washington who broke pro football's racial barrier years later, after World War II. In 1946 he and, later, Strode signed with the Los Angeles Rams—just a few months after Robinson had signed with baseball's Brooklyn Dodgers. In the All-American Football Conference (founded in 1946, the AAFC played rival to the NFL), the Cleveland Browns signed lineman Bill Willis and fullback Marion Motley, both of whom would later be enshrined in the Hall of Fame. Washington might have made it to the Hall, too. But he was already 28 and had un-

cially in the AAFC. Rather than putting the upstart league out of business, the NFL absorbed four franchises and placed the remaining players in a pool to be divided up amongst its own teams. Thus the NFL grew from 9 to 12 teams in 1950, as the Cleveland Browns, 49ers and Baltimore Colts were admitted.

The Cleveland Browns were the class of the AAFC, and they continued to dominate in the NFL. Cleveland fans embraced the Browns wholeheartedly after they re-

dergone surgery on both knees. The Rams knew about this problem, but signed Washington anyway in order to obtain a lease from the Los Angeles Coliseum, which insisted the team open its doors to black players before the Rams could use the stadium. In the end, it was the City of Los Angeles more than the NFL itself that pushed to get blacks into the league. The AAFC was not much better. In the final week of the 1946 season, the Browns left Willis and Motley in Cleveland for their game against the Miami Seahawks. Florida law prohibited "mixed" sporting events, and the AAFC saw no reason to take a stand.

Indeed, change came slowly. By the time the two leagues merged after the 1949 season, there were only 16 black players active in pro football. But during the early part of the 1950s, as more and more colleges were turning out talented black players, that situation began to change. It was no longer just the right thing to do—clearly it was the smart thing to do. The NFL's two best defensive backs ("Night Train" Lane and Emlen Tunnell), its best punter (Horace Gillom), its best kick returners (Buddy Young and Wally Triplett), and one of its best ends (Bob Mann) were black. The teams that met for the NFL championship in 1950 and 1951 (the Browns and Rams) had the most black players. In 1954, the top five rushers in the league were black. And during the 1950s, the two slowest teams to reintegrate (the Bears and Redskins) tumbled into sustained mediocrity.

With more teams and larger rosters in the 1960s, pro football finally began to go after black players in earnest. Although some teams allegedly maintained quotas for black players—and expansion into southern cities such as New Orleans, Atlanta, and Miami created some difficult situations—the percentage of black players in pro football continued to increase.

In 1963, Emlen Tunnell became the first black assistant coach and later the first black player enshrined in the Hall of Fame. In 1965 the league hired its first black field official. In 1966, Buddy Young became the first black to hold an executive position in the NFL commissioner's office. In 1974, Joe Gilliam of the Steelers became the first black quarterback to win a starting NFL job. And in 1989, Art Shell became the league's first black head coach since Fritz Pollard briefly held that position back in the early 1920s.

placed the departed Rams, and the city was overjoyed when they edged the New York Yankees in each of the first two AAFC championship games. The Browns got even better in the AAFC's last two years, going a combined 23–1–2 and trouncing the Buffalo Bisons and 49ers in the two title games.

Cleveland had a marvelous young coach in Paul Brown, and a determined group of former soldiers who went about their business without much emotion or fanfare. The

Paul Brown diagrams a play in 1950. The Cleveland coach had his Browns running like a well-oiled machine in the late 1940s and 1950s; they won four straight AAFC titles, then continued to compete for and win titles after the Browns joined the NFL in 1950.

team's quarterback was Otto Graham, as good a clutch player as has ever played the position. "Automatic Otto" executed the plays sent in by coach Brown. This was highly unusual back then; of course, today, almost every quarterback works that way. Graham was beloved by the fans and, more importantly, by his teammates. Whenever they felt they had nothing left, they could always find a little extra for Otto. Graham, who also played pro basketball, used his athletic prowess on defense as one of the NFL's top safeties.

Graham had two excellent receivers in Dante Lavelli and Mac Speedie. The team's

running star was Marion Motley, a fullback in the Bronko Nagurski mold. Motley was just as big and fast as the Bronk had been, but was a bit more elusive. Whenever the Browns needed big yards, they gave the ball to Motley, and when Graham needed a little extra time to throw he knew he had the best pass-protecting back who ever lived. Rounding out the offense was Lou Groza, who was nicknamed "The Toe." You do not get a nickname like that for giving hot-foots—Groza was the NFL's first great place-kicker. And just to make things more difficult for teams when they did manage to stop the Cleveland offense, punter Horace Gillom had the strongest leg and longest hang time of anyone in the league.

As luck would have it, the 1950 NFL championship game saw the Browns play the Los Angeles Rams—the very team that had left Cleveland fans high and dry in 1946. The Rams were no pushovers. They had reached the NFL title game in 1949, and had the league's best passing attack thanks to Bob Waterfield and Norm Van Brocklin, the two highest-rated quarterbacks in the NFL. Waterfield was the veteran, with six years in the league already. In 1945, he became the first rookie to be named league MVP when he led the Rams to the championship; after the team moved to Los Angeles he became one of the game's highest paid stars. He was also the first quarterback to specialize in throwing the bomb. Waterfield would squeeze off a 50-yard spiral at any time, on any down. This "stretching" of the defense would become standard practice in the NFL a decade or so later, but back in the 1940s Waterfield was the only one who could pull it off. Van Brocklin came to the team in 1949, and the two passers began sharing QB duties a year later, often alter-

Two staples of Cleveland's offense during the 1950s were bruising fullback Marion Motley (here eluding a Pittsburgh tackler) and Lou ("The Toe") Groza, the NFL's first kicking legend. Groza, here sending one through the uprights, was also an all-pro lineman.

nating quarters. An emotional leader with a strong arm, Van Brocklin turned in some unbelievable performances in his years with the Rams, including a 554-yard game and a 41-point quarter.

These two moved the passing game along during the early 1950s, thanks in large part to the helping hands of ends Elroy Hirsch and Tom Fears. Hirsch, whose unorthodox running style earned him the nickname "Crazy Legs," had been a halfback in the AAFC for the Chicago Rockets until he fractured his skull trying to plow through the line. He switched to the receiver position, using his talent for open-field running to befuddle defensive backs both before and

after catches. Fears was Hirsch's opposite. He was a calculating, precise receiver—perfect for clutch third-down plays. He led the league in catches during his first three seasons, and caught 18 balls in one game—both NFL records. In 1950 he racked up 84 receptions, which stood as a league mark for 10 years. The Los Angeles passing game was further assisted by one of the most intriguing quartets of running backs in history: former Heisman Trophy winner Glenn Davis, mighty mite "Vitamin" Smith, and a pair of bull-elephant fullbacks named Dan Towler and Dick Hoerner. Had the Rams ever put a decent defense on the field, they might have gone undefeated.

As expected, the 1950 NFL championship game was a wild one. Los Angeles held a one-point lead until, with 28 second left, Lou Groza booted a 16-yard field goal to hand the Browns the victory, 30-28. To the great delight of the the league, the two teams met for the title again the following year, with Van Brocklin and Fears connecting for a game-winning 73-yard TD. The Browns kept returning to the championship game, making it every year from 1950 to 1957, with the exception of 1956. Paul Brown's system worked so well that even when big stars like Motley, Graham, and Speedie were slowed by age or injuries, there was always a well-coached youngster ready to step in and do the job. The line play of the team was magnificent, with major contributions from such all-time greats as two-way sensation Bill Willis, center Frank Gatski, guard Abe Gibron, defensive linemen Len Ford and Don Colo, and Groza, who was one of the best blockers in the league in the early 1950s, as well as a gifted kicker.

Cleveland's main nemesis during the mid-1950s was the Detroit Lions. Detroit beat Cleveland in the 1952 and 1953 title games, but were blown out by the Browns in the 1954 championship 56-10. The Lions returned the favor when they met again in 1957, fashioning an impressive 59-14 victory despite losing quarterback Bobby Layne to a broken ankle late in the year. Unlike the Browns, the Lions were a wild, undisciplined bunch that played back-alley football as well as any team in history. Layne was the leader on the field, in the locker room, and through the team's frequent all-night celebrations. In practice, he was horrible, unable at times to throw a decent spiral. Once he stepped on the field, however, he became one of the most coura-

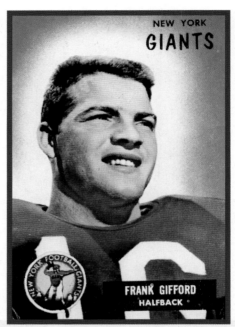

A trading card picturing halfback Frank Gifford. The glamorous Gifford led the New York Giants to the league championship in 1956 and was named MVP.

geous, intelligent field generals the game has ever known. Layne would not accept losing. Indeed, it was said that Bobby never lost a game, time just ran out on him. Layne was joined by a talented cast that included Jack Christiansen, Doak Walker, Joe Schmidt, and Yale Lary. They were not exactly superstars, but when they all played their best the Lions were tough to beat. Other important contributors to this team were linemen Dick Stanfel, Les Bingaman, and two-way star Lou Creekmur.

Although postwar football is fondly remembered for its great quarterbacks, it remained primarily a ground game, and the runners of the late 1940s and 1950s were the ones who ultimately had to carry the load in the pros. Steve Van Buren of the Philadelphia Eagles was the first big name to emerge after the war, and only the second pro in history to go over a thousand yards in a season. Unlike Beattie Feathers, Van Buren did not have a Hall of Famer like Nagurski blocking for him. He was the offensive star of a defensive-minded team that shut out the Chicago Cardinals in 1948 and the Los Angeles Rams in 1949 to win back-to-back NFL championships.

Frank Gifford was a far more glamorous performer. A great all-around player at the University of Southern California, he was drafted by the Giants in 1952 and pressed into immediate service as a defensive back and punt returner. In 1954, an unknown college assistant named Vince Lombardi was hired to jump-start the New York offense, and his first move was to make Giff his halfback. Within two seasons, the Giants were NFL champions and Gifford was the league's MVP.

Strangely, the best backfield of the 1950s never brought its team a championship. From 1952 to 1960, the San Francisco 49ers had Joe "The Jet" Perry and Hugh McElhenney, two of the best running backs in history. As his nickname implies, Perry had incredible acceleration. He was particularly good on screen passes and at powering through narrow openings in the line. McElhenney was a big, tough runner with sneaky moves, wonderful balance, and a knack for breaking off long runs. From 1954 to 1956, these two greats were joined by 225-pound fullback John Henry Johnson, who had won the Canadian Football League MVP award as a rookie in 1953. A devastating blocker, Johnson cleared the way for his teammates, but could also pick up clutch yards himself. Add quarterback Y. A. Tittle to this backfield, and the team had four Hall of Famers!

During the latter half of the 1950s, the Baltimore Colts rose to prominence. The Colts developed the game's next great passer in Johnny Unitas, who had been plucked off the Pittsburgh sandlots after being dumped by the Steelers. The Colts surrounded him with gritty blockers, sure-handed receivers, and a capable running attack. In the span of three short years a franchise that had been the laughing stock of football swept to the Western Conference title. Unitas, who is ranked by many experts as the best all-around quarterback who ever lived, mastered his position completely. When he peered out over the defense before taking the snap, one got the feeling that he was seeing things no one

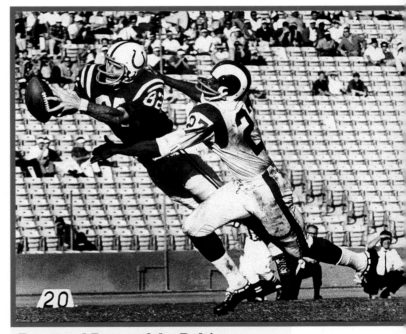

Raymond Berry of the Baltimore Colts reels in the pass that made Johnny Unitas the NFL's career passing-yardage leader in 1966. Unitas and Berry were the deadliest pass combo of their day.

"THE GAME"

Many historians divide professional football into two periods: everything that happened before the 1958 NFL championship game, and everything that happened after it. Most sports fans had felt that the pro game lacked the suspense and drama of a sport like baseball, but this epic battle between the Baltimore Colts and New York Giants—the first NFL title game seen by a national television audience—would change the minds of millions.

The Colts were led by offensive stars Johnny Unitas, Alan Ameche, Lenny Moore, and Raymond Berry, and featured a tough, opportunistic defense. They were lunch-bucket guys coming into Yankee Stadium to take on the glitzy Giants, league champions just two years earlier. New York's Frank Gifford coughed up two first-half fumbles that led to a pair of Baltimore touchdowns and a 14-3 halftime lead. The Giants reached the end zone twice in the second half to grab a 17-14 lead, but Unitas worked his way into field-goal range and the Colts tied the game with seven seconds left. For the first time, an official NFL game went into overtime. The tension was excruciating. The Giants received the kickoff but failed to put any points on the board. Unitas got the ball on his own 20-yard line, and then methodically worked his way downfield on a spine-tingling 12-play drive. From the one-yard line, Ameche took a handoff and barreled into the end zone for the win.

The 1958 title game turned the world on to professional football. All anyone could talk about was "The Game," and long after the season was over the NFL was a hot topic of conversation. The league had signed a television deal with CBS in 1956, and the timing could not have been any better, for it enabled the NFL to develop a national following by 1958. After the sudden-death classic, America was hooked on pro football.

Johnny Unitas gets plenty of pass protection on this play during "The Game." The dramatic, nationally televised 1958 NFL Championship Game got millions of Americans hooked on pro football.

else saw. Unitas always seemed to call the right play, and he knew when to gamble and when it was time to play it safe. Pressure had no effect on him, and he just could not be intimidated; he stayed in the pocket and absorbed vicious hits when other quarterbacks would have panicked and run. For his part, Unitas did not claim to have the best arm or the most analytical mind. His approach, in fact, was very basic: The defense always gives you something, so take what they give you.

Unitas worked especially hard on his timing, as did his favorite receiver, Raymond Berry. Together, they perfected a series of sideline pass plays that were practically unstoppable. Berry would come off the line, run to a predetermined area, and break a quick move on his man. While this was happening, Unitas would already be zipping the ball to the precise spot he knew Berry would arrive at. When Unitas needed tough yards, he handed the ball to Alan "The Horse" Ameche, a fullback who was every bit as powerful as his nickname implied. To really shake things up, however, Unitas would call Lenny Moore's number. Moore was a lightning-quick halfback with great moves and a good pair of hands. In 1958, he ran the ball 82 times and averaged a whopping 7.3 yards per carry, and hauled in 50 passes for an average of 18.8 yards per catch, scoring a total of 14 touchdowns. The Colts defense featured some of the roughest players in the league, including tackles Art Donovan and Big Daddy Lipscomb, ends Don Joyce and Ordell Braase, and linebackers Don Shinnick and Bill Pellington. The best of the group, Gino Marchetti, is still rated by many as the best defensive end ever to play. Baltimore won the 1958 NFL championship game with a dramatic overtime victory against the Gi-

ants, and closed out the decade by beating the New Yorkers for the title again in 1959.

College Football in the 1960s

More so than in any previous decade, college football in the 1960s was characterized by individuals who personally took control of games by dominating their positions. The top quarterbacks riddled secondaries with bullet passes, the top runners tore through front lines for huge gains, and the best defensive players were making tackles all over the field. The game was growing more and more sophisticated, and there was an unprecedented amount of raw talent with which to work. Black players, who saw relatively few scholarships from big-time football programs during the 1940s and 1950s, were now being heavily recruited by all but a few schools, and this dramatically raised the level of play.

College football was also starting to become what many feel it is today: a training ground for future pros. With a new league bidding for the best players, the financial incentives for pursuing a professional career were greater than ever. In fact, many colleges talked high-school stars into playing for them by saying that they would be exposed to professional-caliber systems. Often they were telling the truth—passing plays may have been a little more sophisticated in the NFL and AFL, but in many other ways the college and pro games were remarkably similar.

The 1960s saw several excellent programs rise and fall. The dominant team of the decade, however, was the University of Alabama. Coach Paul "Bear" Bryant knew how to teach his players winning football, and he produced a pair of great quarter-

THE BIRTH OF THE AFL

The immense popularity of professional football in the late 1950s did not escape the attention of millionaires Lamar Hunt and Bud Adams. Each man was willing to put up big bucks for a new NFL franchise in 1959, but they were flatly refused. The NFL was happy and healthy as a 12-team league, and it did not need a couple of hot-shot oil men invading its ranks. After their applications were turned down, Hunt and Adams decided to form their own league. In the summer of 1959 they met with a group of investors and laid out plans for the American Football League.

When the 1960 season started, there were eight new pro football teams. The AFL added a few important wrinkles to its product in order to be more fan-friendly than the NFL: each player's name appeared on the back of his uniform; the scoreboard clock became the official game clock; and after scoring a touchdown teams were given the option of kicking the extra point or going for the end zone again—the two-point conversion. The franchise owners had enough money to let the league develop and even withstand a few years of empty seats. The AFL also had a national television contract that would guarantee enough cash for each team to cover its basic expenses. Hunt and his fellow pioneers knew starting a new pro league would not be easy, but they knew it could be done.

backs in Joe Namath and Ken Stabler. From 1963 to 1967, the Crimson Tide won three national championships and did not drop a single home game. From 1960 to 1969, the team lost a total of just 16 games. Bryant's secret lay in his keen sense of what it took to motivate individual players. If one fellow needed to be told how much he was liked and respected by his teammates, that's what Bryant told him. If another needed his rear end kicked, the Bear was happy to oblige. He even suspended his best player—Joe Namath, who was caught drinking in violation of team rules—at the climax of the 1964 season, with one regular-season game left to play

and then the Sugar Bowl against archrival Mississippi. 'Bama won them both.

Bryant also took what he had and made the best of things, rather than forcing players to follow a set system. When he had good blockers, he ran a ball-control offense. When he had a good passer, he switched to a passing attack. Although he produced no Heisman Trophy winners, Bryant did turn out several players who went on to be all-stars in the pros.

The standout offensive players of the 1960s were almost all running backs. The University of Southern California's O. J. Simpson was the best, leading the country in rushing with 1,415 yards in 1967 and

The legendary Alabama coach Bear Bryant on November 14, 1981, the day he tied Amos Alonzo Stagg for most all-time college coaching wins.

running ability, and there was no better field leader in all of college football. He won the starting job as a sophomore and completed an unheard-of 67 percent of his passes to lead the nation. That performance was no fluke; in 1963 he again connected on two out of every three passes, leading Navy to a 9–1 record and getting the school closer to a national championship than ever before. During that spectacular season, Staubach earned the nickname "Roger the Dodger" for his magnificent scrambling ability. Navy did not have a great line, so he was flushed from the pocket as many as 15 times a game. This created real problems for the defense, because when Staubach charged down the field he had the size, speed, and courage of a fullback. Indeed, he gained over 400 rushing yards in 1963—most of

1,709 in 1968. A big back with explosive speed, Simpson had the nimble feet of a much smaller man, plus a weird ability to sense where unseen tacklers were when he was galloping in the open field. Prior to Simpson, Gale Sayers of Kansas University was the country's most heralded runner. He rushed for more than 1,000 yards as a sophomore, and then led the nation with 7.9 yards per carry as a senior. Sayers had tremendous speed and instincts, and a cutback move that left would-be tacklers grabbing armfuls of air.

The best quarterback of the 1960s was Roger Staubach of the United States Naval Academy. He had a great arm, tremendous

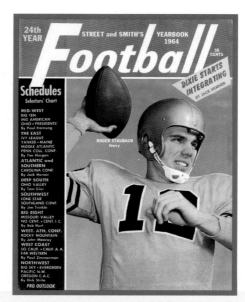

Navy's Roger Staubach was the top college quarterback story of the 1960s, winning the Heisman Trophy in 1963. He went on to guide the Dallas Cowboys to three Super Bowl appearances.

them on busted plays—and earned the Heisman Trophy.

The 1960s saw a new generation of bigger, quicker defensive players come to college football, and they could affect a ball game just as dramatically as the Simpsons and Staubachs. Bubba Smith of Michigan State University was a 6'8" 280-pound monster with a bad attitude. He was as quick as players 6 inches shorter and 60 pounds lighter, which meant that no one could handle him. When Smith wanted to make a point he would tackle a ball carrier by picking him up and dropping him on his head. Sometimes he would grab a blocker

Gargantuan defensive lineman Bubba Smith first terrorized quarterbacks while playing for the Michigan State Spartans and then for the NFL's Baltimore Colts and Oakland Raiders.

and a ball carrier with his long arms and throw them both to the ground. When Spartans fans started chanting "Kill Bubba Kill," no one on the other team wanted to go near the ball for fear of what he might do to them. Defensive tackle Buck Buchanan of Grambling State University was also a big, bad dude. And he was even faster than Smith. His favorite move was to drive an offensive lineman straight backwards, knocking over the ball carrier or quarterback. Buchanan also had a little spin move that left his man eating turf and gave him a clear shot at the ball.

The linebacker position also began yielding superstar players. Lee Roy Jordan was a standout for Bear Bryant's Alabama teams, two-way star Dick Butkus of the University of Illinois was a top linebacker and All-American center, and Willie Lanier made national headlines with his play at Morgan State University. But the glamour boy of the position was Tommy Nobis of the University of Texas. At 6'4" and 240 pounds he could hold his own in the trenches. Yet he was also quick enough to blanket running backs going out for short passes. He hit hard and he played smart, instantly recognizing blocking schemes thanks to his dual role as the Longhorn center. His blitzing ruined Joe Namath's final college game, as Texas upset Alabama 21-17 in the Orange Bowl.

The Pro Football War

The American Football League probably could have survived had it merely mimicked the NFL. Pro football had won millions of new fans during the late 1950s, and there were certainly enough paying customers to support two leagues. The AFL's owners, however, had something a lot more ambitious in mind: They wanted their league to be just as good as the NFL. It would take many years and a lot of cash to build up an equal amount of talent, so in the short run the AFL settled for putting a more exciting brand of football on the field. And that meant plenty of passing.

In the years following World War II, a generation of players had grown up learning to throw and catch the football. In fact, many high-school and college teams had developed passing attacks every bit as complex as those used in the NFL. But with only 12 NFL teams during the 1950s, quarterback jobs were very hard to come by, and many talented passers were cut because their teams did not believe they could get the job done. In reality, a lot of those quarterbacks were simply ahead of their times. It takes more than a strong arm, good eyes, and quick thinking to be a successful passer—it also takes smart, talented receivers and an offensive line that knows how to build a pocket of protection around its quarterback. A lot of potential stars failed in the NFL because whenever they faded back to pass, their teammates allowed them to be overwhelmed by the defense. The AFL specifically sought out these players. The owners recognized that the older league had been wasting a very precious resource, and after just a few seasons the upstart league had some of the best arms in pro football. In 1960, the AFL signed George Blanda, Al Dorow, Jack Kemp, Cotton Davidson, Frank Tripucka, and Babe Parili—each of whom had been discarded by at least one NFL franchise during the previous decade, and most of whom had sought refuge in the pass-oriented Canadian Football League.

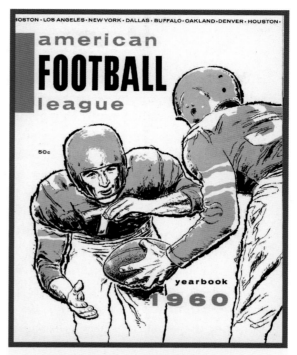

The American Football League's yearbook for its inaugural 1960 season. By luring away big-name players and encouraging an entertaining, pass-happy style of play, the AFL mounted the most successful challenge to the NFL's pro-football supremacy.

Blanda had actually been forced to retire by the Chicago Bears, who felt he was washed up in 1959 at the age of 31. After sitting out a year, he signed with the Houston Oilers and led the team to the AFL championship game three years in a row. Blanda teamed with halfback Billy Cannon, who represented the league's first major victory against the NFL. It had been assumed that Cannon, the 1959 Heisman Trophy winner, would sign with an established NFL team. But the Oilers threw $100,000 at his feet and he decided to join the AFL. Charley Hennigan, the team's best receiver,

THE BOY CZAR

Historians will argue forever about exactly when it was that professional football became the most popular sport in the United States. But they can certainly agree that a disagreement among NFL owners was the best thing ever to happen to the game. In 1960, the search for a successor to deceased commissioner Bert Bell bogged down after two highly qualified candidates were nominated. As a sort of compromise, the owners installed a 33-year-old named Pete Rozelle, who had previously served as general manager of the Los Angeles Rams. Rozelle was instructed to fight off the challenge of the American Football League with whatever means he deemed necessary. But instead of attacking the new league he concentrated on strengthening the NFL.

Under Rozelle, the Cardinals moved from crowded Chicago to more fertile territory in St. Louis, and the league expanded into Minneapolis and Dallas, driving away AFL franchises in both cities. He also convinced owners that the NFL would be stronger if the owners banded together and sold their television rights to a network in a package deal, rather than peddling their games to local affiliates. Rozelle then went before Congress and convinced them to pass a bill making such a "monopoly" legal.

When faced with internal troubles, Rozelle was swift and decisive. When superstars Paul Hornung and Alex Karras were implicated in a betting scandal he kicked them out of football, and fined the Detroit Lions for failing to control several other players accused of gambling. He even disciplined old-time owners George Preston Marshall and George Halas when they got out of line.

Rozelle clearly was not a man who shrank from a challenge. But he was wise enough to know when working things out with the enemy was smarter than escalating the war. Rozelle recognized that the AFL had been very clever in developing itself as a rival league, and when he felt that its teams were approaching NFL caliber, he put in motion a plan to absorb them. Why spend millions trying to destroy the AFL, Rozelle believed, especially when they would pay millions to join the NFL?

Rozelle was an expert in marketing and public relations, and he refocused the commissioner's office on enhancing the image and value of the NFL and its franchises. He formed relationships with the television networks and other corporate partners that helped pro football become the most popular sport in America. Initially ridiculed as the "boy czar," Rozelle was a major reason why the same NFL franchises that could be had for a million dollars or less in 1960 were worth over $100 million when he retired in 1989.

Football always was and always will be a violently physical game, as this 1964 photograph of battered Giants quarterback Y. A. Tittle shows. Tittle never really regained his form after this devastating sack.

touchdown passes with 36, and he took the Oilers to their second-straight league title.

The NFL watched the AFL's air show with great interest and more than a little concern. Soon, many NFL teams were taking to the air as never before, and also hanging on to strong-armed quarterbacks, even if they were just bench-warmers. Len Dawson was one of the last to escape. A passer with the rare combination of mobility and accuracy, he had sat on the bench for the Steelers and Browns during six NFL seasons. When Cleveland cut Dawson during training camp in the summer of 1962, his old coach at Purdue University, Hank Stram, invited him to try out for his Dallas Texans. The rest is history. The Texans won the AFL championship that year as Dawson threw out of Stram's "moving pocket" for 29 touchdowns. The Texans moved north and became the Kansas City Chiefs, and as the decade progressed, Dawson became the leader of one of the most balanced and successful teams in football, finishing the 1960s with no less than three AFL championships.

With the pipeline of NFL discards and second-stringers starting to close, the AFL had to outbid the NFL for top college quarterbacks. This began a decade-long competition that created a dramatic rise in salaries and ultimately sowed the seeds of a merger between the two leagues. John Hadl was the first "home-grown" AFL passing star. Drafted out of Kansas University by the San Diego Chargers in 1962, he sat behind veteran Tobin Rote for a couple of seasons before blossoming into a superstar. Hadl teamed with an exciting young flanker named Lance Alworth to form the AFL's deadliest passing tandem. In 1963, the Buffalo Bills drafted Notre Dame's Daryl Lam-

had been teaching high school biology in 1959. He taped his final paycheck to the inside of his helmet, and whenever he needed a little extra incentive during games, he would look at it. As was the case with most other AFL squads, the supporting players came from the CFL, the sandlots, and everywhere else football was being played. NFL fans used Blanda's 1960 resurrection as proof that the AFL was a second-rate outfit, and when he lost his job in training camp the following year, it seemed as if they might have been right. But he won back the starting role six games into the season and proceeded to smash the pro record for

onica, who had an arm like a cannon. He shared time with Kemp in 1964 and 1966, helping the Bills to the AFL championship game each season. In 1967, Lamonica was acquired by the Oakland Raiders for two established stars. The risky trade paid off as his long-range bombing guided his new team to division titles in five of the next six seasons.

The biggest coup for the AFL, however, was the signing of Alabama star Joe Namath. Good-looking, talented, and confident, Namath was a perfect advertisement for the upstart league. He was signed by the New York Jets, meaning the AFL's most recognized player would be doing his thing in the country's biggest football market.

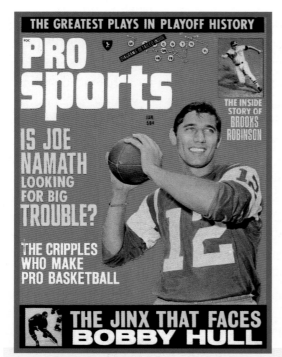

The AFL's New York Jets made front-page news in 1965 when they signed Alabama's star quarterback Joe Namath, as this cover from *Pro Sports* magazine shows.

Namath signed a huge and highly publicized contract, and proceeded to pick AFL pass defenses apart. The Jets had little else in the way of offensive weapons other than "Broadway Joe," but when he was on, there was no way to stop him. Namath could drill the ball through the tiniest opening, or float a feathery pass right into the hands of a streaking receiver. And when he got a man open deep, Namath could wing the ball 50 yards, even off-balance. By 1967, he was working his magic with wideout George Sauer, flanker Don Maynard, and Pete Lammons, a burly tight end. That year he amassed 4,007 yards through the air. In 1968, Namath took the Jets to the AFL title.

The NFL did not lose out on all the best quarterbacks during the 1960s. Sonny Jurgensen of the Eagles and Redskins was one of the great pure passers in football history. A backup for Philadelphia during the late 1950s, he took over in 1961 and had a fabulous season, setting a record for passing yards and tying the league mark of 32 touchdowns. Had he not missed time due to injury, he would have racked up more passing yards than anyone during the 1960s. The NFL's second expansion team of the 1960s, the Minnesota Vikings, handed their passing duties over to University of Georgia graduate Fran Tarkenton. Minnesota's offensive line was so bad that Tarkenton rarely had time to set up and wait for his receivers to get open. Luckily, the youngster had a knack for sensing and side-stepping danger, as well as an ability to scramble around and throw on the run. Tarkenton's ability to turn broken plays into first downs made him one of the league's most dangerous weapons, but throughout the 1960s he had terrible teams around him, and in six years with the

Vikings and three with the Giants, he produced only one winning season.

The NFL's version of Joe Namath was John Brodie of the San Francisco 49ers. He too was good looking, talented, and charismatic. An All-American at Stanford University in 1956, he was drafted by San Francisco but did not become a full-time starter until 1961. During the mid-1960s he was always among the league's most highly regarded passers, but he could not turn his shaky supporting cast into a consistent winner. Still, in 1967, the AFL went after him very aggressively. The Houston Oilers offered him a $250,000 salary, a car dealership, and several other bonuses if he were willing to jump leagues. The 49ers countered with a four-year deal that paid him more than $200,000 a year for four years. Things were getting crazy, and both leagues knew it. It would not be long before all the top quarterbacks were making more than a quarter-million dollars a year, and soon the best runners, receivers, linebackers, and pass rushers would be playing the AFL and

NFL off each other for big money. One can only wonder what Johnny Unitas would have commanded on the open market. He remained football's top quarterback throughout the 1960s, keeping the Colts in the thick of things even as the great Baltimore team of the late 1950s began to disintegrate around him. He played in seven Pro Bowls during the 1960s, and passed for more yards than anyone else during the decade.

Although the 1960s saw professional football mature into something very close to its present form, the big news in the sport during the decade was made by the Green Bay Packers, a team that specialized in old-time, slug-mouth football. From 1961 to 1967, the Packers were nearly invincible. The team was coached by Vince Lombardi, who had toiled as a college and pro assistant for more than a decade. During this time he had become convinced that the key to a great offense was not designing hundreds of plays, but running a dozen or so to absolute perfection. It was his contention that a basic

Vince Lombardi gets maximum effort out of his players as they hit the blocking sleds. Lombardi's Green Bay Packer teams were famed for their discipline and work ethic, and it paid off with six trips to the NFL title game in eight seasons.

sweep around end was guaranteed to gain five or more yards if each player did his job—even if the other team knew it was coming. Lombardi had been one of Fordham University's legendary linemen during the 1930s. He got the job done not with brute strength but by intelligence and finesse, and he expected nothing less of his Packers.

When Lombardi took over Green Bay in 1959, the team had several players who fit this description, yet they had won just one game the year before. Lombardi discarded those he felt did not have a winning attitude, picked up some hungry youngsters to fill out the roster, and began to teach a core of tough, smart players the Lombardi style of football. He drilled the Packers unmercifully, playing no favorites and accepting no

excuses for a bad performance. As one player put it, Lombardi treated all of the Packers the same: like dogs. In 1959, the same group of players who had gone 1–10–1 the year before finished an impressive 7–5. In 1960, Green Bay went to the league championship game, barely losing to the Eagles. And in 1961, they destroyed the Giants 37-0 to win the NFL title. Often criticized for taking the imagination out of football, Lombardi was hailed by those who knew the game because he ran the kind of basic plays that let a player use his imagination. Each Packer knew his role so well that if something went wrong during a play, someone could almost always improvise and fix it.

The Packer offense was led by Jim Taylor, Paul Hornung, and Bart Starr. Taylor

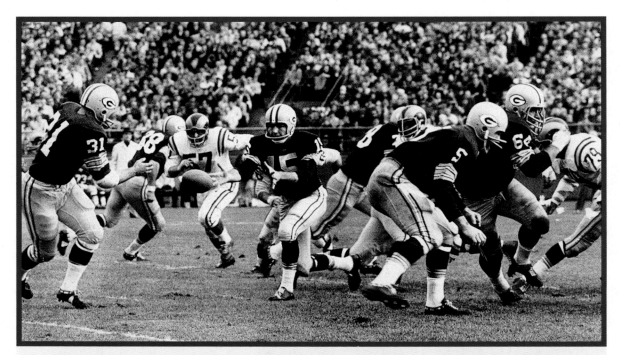

Green Bay launches its bread-and-butter play, the sweep. Quarterback Bart Starr pitches the ball to Jim Taylor (31), while Paul Hornung (5), Jerry Kramer (64), and Norm Masters (78) look for their blocks.

The linebacker-sized but fearsomely quick Jim Brown steams ahead against the Philadelphia Eagles in 1963.

was the backfield's blunt instrument, a rock-solid fullback who was practically impossible to tackle one-on-one. When he did get nailed, he would sneer at the other guy and ask him if that was as hard as he could hit. Hornung was Green Bay's point-scoring machine, a halfback who could run, throw, and kick the football. Lombardi loved these two, for they reminded him of the players he knew back in the 1930s. The man who put the offense into motion was Bart Starr. A mild-mannered quarterback who matched his considerable skills to the specific needs of the Packer system, he was a masterful play caller and a deadly accurate passer. He seemed to know when the defense was totally keyed into Taylor and Hornung, at which times he would deliver the ball to one of his receivers for a big gain. These three played behind what may have been the best bunch of offensive linemen ever assembled on one team. Jim Ringo handled chores at center, Fuzzy Thurston and Jerry Kramer played magnificently at guard, and Forrest Gregg led a group of talented tackles.

The Packer stars during the 1960s also included several defensive standouts. Willie Davis stuffed runs and harassed opposing passers from his post at defensive end, while linebacker Ray Nitschke ranked among the best run-stoppers and hardest tacklers ever to play. The defensive backfield was anchored by Willie Wood, who many feel is the finest free safety of all time, and cornerback Herb Adderley, who outplayed the other team's top receiver in practically every game of his career. This group remained more or less intact for eight seasons. During that time, the Packers went to the championship game an amazing six times, winning the NFL title on five occasions.

The NFL's most important player during the 1960s was running back Jim Brown of the Cleveland Browns. He combined size, speed, toughness, and durability better than any football player before or since, and he revolutionized the game in a number of ways. Brown came out of Syracuse University in 1957 as one of the best all-around athletes this country ever produced. He could have starred in the NBA, competed in the Olympics, fought as a heavyweight boxing contender, or played major-league baseball. He was also the best lacrosse player anyone has ever seen. But Brown chose football, and by all accounts he made the right decision. As a rookie he shattered the NFL's single-game rushing record, and led the league in yards gained. During his eight-year career, he was the top ground gainer a remarkable seven times, and in 1964 he led the Browns to the NFL championship.

The emergence of Jim Brown set in motion some interesting forces in pro football. At first, team owners went in search of 6'2" 230-pound running backs with sprinter's speed, but they soon realized that Brown was unique. Instead, they began looking for linebackers with the size and mobility to stop Brown. This group included beefed-up defensive backs, slimmed-down offensive linemen, and big college running backs who were perhaps a step too slow to be impact players in the pros.

None of these bizarre fantasies, however, could compare to the reality of Dick Butkus. Butkus was the meanest, dirtiest, fastest, roughest, craziest defensive player to ever step on a football field. He came into Chicago Bears camp in the summer of 1965, and by the first game he had taken the starting middle linebacker job away from All-Pro Bill George. When Butkus tackled ball carriers, he gave them a violent twist as he threw them to the ground, then he would rip the ball from their hands and claim he had recovered a fumble. When rushing the passer, he would launch himself through the air, often flying over startled blockers. In pass coverage, Butkus would brutalize running backs who dared to venture into his

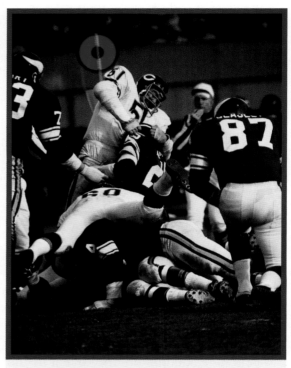

Linebacker Dick Butkus was a wild man every time he stepped on a football field, as this photograph of him trying to unscrew a Minnesota running back's head shows.

territory. And before the ball was snapped, he would spit on offensive linemen. Teams playing the Bears spent most of the week trying to decide how to best avoid him.

Chicago's opponents, when not worrying about Butkus, wracked their brains trying to stop Gale Sayers, who ranks as the single most exciting player of the 1960s. A running back and return man out of Kansas University, he came to the Bears the same year as Butkus and set the league on fire. Sayers was fast and slippery, but what set him apart from other runners was his ability to cut sideways and then continue downfield without sacrificing any speed. He was one of a handful of players in NFL history

With his speed and astonishing moves, Gale Sayers of the Chicago Bears was a threat to score every time he carried the ball.

who was a legitimate threat to score any time he touched the ball. He led the league in rushing twice despite the fact that, as Chicago's lone offensive weapon, he had the full attention of the defense on almost every play. To this day, Sayers is revered among running backs, and old films of his magnificent runs still bring fans to their feet.

College Football in the 1970s

During the 1970s pro football finally caught up to the college game in terms of fan interest and overall popularity. From the stand-

point of the NCAA, this was not necessarily a bad development. On the contrary, college football was helped immensely by the money being generated by the NFL. Football itself was exploding, entering the decade as America's most popular spectator sport. And everyone, it seemed, was getting a big slice of the pie. Television coverage of college contests generated millions for universities and the networks, and the game was starting to be "marketed" in a very sophisticated manner. Schools worked hard to develop an image that would draw national attention. If a college had a legendary coach, then he was the big selling point. If there was a Heisman Trophy candidate on campus, the athletic department worked hard to keep him in the public eye. Even if a team had an unknown coach and unspectacular players, it could still promote itself as a "system" or "program" if it was winning consistently.

The television networks, newspapers, and sports magazines played right along. Football fans were devouring information as never before, and competition for their attention was fierce. The top college stars, in fact, were treated in the media as if they were just auditioning for the pros—establishing a connection that drew millions of NFL fans into the college game. The days when a fan could turn on cable TV and tune into any one of a dozen games was still many years away, but the foundation for this level of interest was already being built.

For most of the 1970s college ball was still a ground-oriented game, with only a few schools running complex passing offenses. With players getting bigger, faster, and stronger it made more sense to hand the ball to one man and let his teammates clear a path than it did to rely on a quarterback and

Truce!

In the early 1960s, the American Football League took on the National Football League with patience and intelligence. It paid big salaries to a few key college players, but otherwise left NFL rosters alone. The AFL concentrated on putting good teams on the field, and disguised its manpower weaknesses by promoting its game as more open and exciting. By the middle of the decade, the AFL had a large national television audience and several home-grown stars. With loyal fans and a more-or-less steady flow of cash, the new league began to get aggressive.

When the New York Giants signed Buffalo kicker Pete Gogolak following the 1965 season, AFL commissioner Al Davis believed that the NFL was preparing to sink his league by stealing away its best players. In retaliation, he targeted several NFL stars and urged AFL clubs to sign them to big deals. The AFL also escalated the bidding war over college talent, driving up salaries and upsetting the balance of power in the NFL. Adding to the tension between the two leagues was the amazing drawing power of New York Jets quarterback Joe Namath. In his first game, "Broadway Joe" drew more than 50,000 fans to a game against the Oilers—in Texas! Namath's sex appeal, confidence, and tremendous talent made him the darling of the media in football's most important city at a time when the Giants were going through a period of mediocrity.

Prior to the 1966 season, NFL commissioner Pete Rozelle revealed that secret talks had been held and that a merger agreement between the two leagues had been hammered out. The AFL clubs would officially join the NFL in 1970, paying approximately $2 million each for the privilege—an amount they would easily recoup with the added revenues from television and the savings in payroll now that the salary wars were over. And the fans would get a special treat that winter: the "Super Bowl," an official game played between the AFL champ and the NFL champ.

Super Bowl I was played between the Green Bay Packers and Kansas City Chiefs, and as most everyone expected, Bart Starr and company won handily. The same thing happened in Super Bowl II, as the Packers blew out the Oakland Raiders. As the merger date approached, there was some question as to whether the deal had actually diluted pro

In 1966, the costly war between the AFL and the NFL came to an end. From left, NFL president Tex Schramm, NFL commissioner Pete Rozelle, and AFL founder Lamar Hunt announce the merger of the two leagues.

football. A lot of NFL owners did not want to be stuck playing AFL teams that their fans considered second-rate.

As Super Bowl III approached, the skies grew especially dark. The Baltimore Colts, with their high-powered offense and bone-crunching defense, were to meet the cocky, young Jets. As the two teams began practicing for the game in Miami, most experts predicted the Colts would win by two touchdowns. The Jets became 19-point underdogs when Namath did the one thing you never do in sports: guarantee a victory. It was all the Colt players could do to stop themselves from assaulting Namath before the Super Bowl, but once the game started it was a different story. The New York defense was more stubborn than expected, the Baltimore offense missed a couple of golden opportunities, and Namath dissected Baltimore's heralded defense with perfect play-calling and clutch passes. Although the final score was

Joe Namath leaves the field a champion after the Jets beat the heavily favored Colts in Super Bowl III. The victory erased any notion that AFL football was inferior to the game the NFL offered.

16-7, the Colts never seemed to be in the game. With their victory in Super Bowl III, the Jets had earned for the AFL all the respect it needed to make the merger go smoothly, paving the way for peace and prosperity—and some remarkable football—in the decade that followed.

a receiver hooking up on a risky pass play. Indeed, the three dominant college programs of the 1970s specialized in wearing down opponents at the line of scrimmage and gobbling up territory a few yards at a time.

Alabama had another great run under Bear Bryant, winning between 9 and 12 games a season from 1971 to 1979. The

Crimson Tide went to a bowl game every year during the 1970s and won the national championship in 1973, 1978, and 1979. Bryant used the same formula he had in the 1960s, maximizing the talents of each team and minimizing its weaknesses. In the early 1970s the Tide got great line play from tackles John Hannah and Buddy Brown,

FEARSOME FOURSOMES

Although football had always been a game dominated by the defense, it was not until the arrival of the offensive stars of the 1960s that the game had its first famous *defensive* "front fours." The four-man line had come into wide use during the 1950s, as the linebacker position became more important and teams stopped using six- and seven-man defensive fronts. The idea behind using a front four was to put pressure on the quarterback when he passed, and bottle up running plays long enough for the linebackers and defensive backs to jump in and finish things off.

The New York Giants and Baltimore Colts won NFL championships with great defensive quartets, but the first group to actually earn a nickname was the San Diego Charger "Fearsome Foursome" of Ron Nery, Earl Faison, Dick Hudson, and Ernie Ladd. This group anchored the AFL's first great defense and helped the Chargers win a pair of division titles. After this unit broke up, the Detroit Lions put together a front four of Alex Karras, Roger Brown, Sam Williams, and Darris McCord. They too were known as the "Fearsome Foursome." In 1966, the Los Angeles Rams went from worst to first in the NFL's Western Conference on the strength of its

The Fearsome Foursome—from left, Merlin Olsen (74), Lamar Lundy (hidden), Deacon Jones (75), and Roger Brown (78)—in hot pursuit of a ball carrier.

front four of Deacon Jones, Merlin Olsen, Rosey Grier (and later, Roger Brown), and Lamar Lundy, who averaged 6'5" and 270 pounds. Unlike their predecessors, this "Fearsome Foursome" featured a superstar at each position—and out of reverence no one used the nickname again.

Jones was not only the league's top sack man (he had 52 during one two-year span) he actually invented the term "sack." He also used the now-illegal head slap with tooth-loosening effectiveness. Jones was big and fast, but what separated him from other defensive ends was his tenacity. He never stopped trying until the whistle blew, often making tackles after he had been driven to the ground and left for dead. Olsen, who is rated by many as the best defensive tackle in history, took a more measured approach. He analyzed his opponent during the course of a game, and developed moves he could use in the final quarter when a big tackle or quarterback sack could mean the difference in a tight game. Defensive tackle Grier was a graduate of the Giant front four of the 1950s, but still lightning-quick off the line, while the 6'7" Lundy could harass the passer or lay off the rush and back up his linemates. Working as a unit, these four usually teamed for around 50 sacks a year and allowed the fewest yards per carry in the NFL.

blowing open holes for a group of workmanlike runners headed by Wilbur Jackson. In the middle of the decade, Alabama suffocated teams with a touchdown-a-game defense led by linebacker Woodrow Lowe, defensive tackle Bob Baumhower, and defensive end Leroy Cook. By the end of the 1970s, coach Bryant had a little of everything, including quarterbacks Jeff Rutledge and Steadman Shealey, wideout Ozzie Newsome, and running backs Tony Nathan and Major Ogilvie. The offensive line featured Dwight Stephenson, Jim Bunch, and Mike Brock, while the defensive front included ferocious Marty Lyons and slashing run-stopper E. J. Junior.

The University of Southern California had a couple of tough years after O. J. Simpson graduated, but by 1971 the team was right back in the hunt for a national title. Over the next nine seasons, USC produced four of the finest runners ever to play in Sam Cunningham, Anthony Davis, Ricky Bell, and Charles White. Cunningham, whose younger brother Randall would star in the NFL during the 1980s, slammed through the line for big yards behind the blocking of All-Americans Pete Adams and John Vella. Davis became a household name after scoring six touchdowns against Notre Dame in 1972, the same year that he and Cunningham formed a backfield that took USC to the national championship. The 5'9" Davis topped 1,000 yards in each of his three varsity seasons, and averaged more than 150 all-purpose yards per game. Bell took over ball-carrying duties for the Trojans in 1975, and with the help of linemen Marvin Powell and Joe Davis, outdid his two predecessors by leading the nation with 1,875 yards as a junior. A huge running back, Bell actually played linebacker as a freshman in 1973. White teamed with Bell as a freshman, then became USC's main man in his sophomore year. He gained nearly 5,000 yards in three seasons as a starter, including 1,803 in 1979 to lead the nation and capture Heisman Trophy.

At Oklahoma University 35-year-old Barry Switzer took over in 1973 and led his Sooners to a pair of national championships in 1974 and 1975. The Sooners were in contention for the number-one spot in college football every year after that, thanks to great running and tough defense. Switzer inherited a team that had just graduated 1,000-yard runner Greg Pruitt, and had several more holes to plug. He made 5'9" sophomore Joe Washington his new go-to guy and Washington responded with back-to-back 1,000-yard seasons. The defense starred the Selmon brothers—Lucious, Dewey, and Lee Roy—each of whom earned All-America recognition. After the two national titles, the Sooners stayed in the Top 10 by moving the pile on offense and stuffing all comers on defense. Oklahoma never did reach the top of the rankings again, but the school was not without a national superstar. That honor belonged to Billy Sims, who led all college runners with 160 yards a game in 1978, and led the nation in total rushing yards in 1979. During those two seasons, the Sooners lost only twice, and Sims scored an incredible 42 touchdowns. He won the Heisman Trophy in 1978 and finished second in 1979.

Billy Sims and Charles White were great backs. But the three Heisman Trophy winners preceding them were even better. Ohio State University knew it had a special player in Archie Griffin when he ran for 772 yards as a freshman in 1972. And many Buckeye fans were disappointed when he did not win the Heisman Trophy after nearly doubling that total as a sophomore. They were not disappointed the next two years, however, when the 5'9" Griffin became the first player to win back-to-back Heismans, and the first to run for over 100 yards in more than 30 consecutive games. He had great instincts, incredible balance, and a combination of speed and moves that left tacklers groping helplessly as he breezed past them. All that eluded him was a national championship, which the Buckeyes lost in the 1976 Rose Bowl, his final game.

Tony Dorsett did some rewriting of the record books, too. As a University of Pittsburgh freshman, he gained 1,586 yards and put the Panther program back on the college

Pittsburgh running back Tony Dorsett appears to have this defender overmatched. Dorsett had his way with nearly every college defense—he ran for well over 1,000 yards in each of his four seasons.

football map. He topped the 1,000-yard mark as a sophomore and junior, then had a season for the ages in 1976, when he came within 52 yards of gaining 2,000. Dorsett was the first college back of the 1970s who was unquestionably playing at a level high enough to move right into a starring role in the pros. He stood just under six feet tall and weighed around 180 pounds. He could take a lot of punishment on short-yardage downs, slice quickly through openings when he had the blocking, and was deceptively fast in the open field. Dorsett would take a handoff, pick a hole and then explode. His patented move was a two-footed stop, which would enable him to spring back in the other direction. To make matters worse for Pitt's opponents, Dorsett could also catch the ball coming out of the backfield. Indeed, in 1975 he grabbed 11 passes for three touchdowns and averaged more than 17 yards per reception.

In 1977, the football world focused its attention on the University of Texas, where big, bad Earl Campbell was making pro scouts drool. A 1,000-yard rusher as a sophomore, he was cut down by an injury in his junior year, but bounced back magnificently to lead the nation with 1,744 rushing yards. Campbell was built to run the ball. He had quick feet, huge thighs, great speed, and a low center of gravity. Time and time again he would barrel through the line and magically emerge five yards later with two or three defenders desperately holding on to him. No one—not even Jim Brown—put a hurt on tacklers the way Campbell did. The Longhorns went undefeated in Campbell's Heisman season, but lost their chance at a national title when they were beaten 38-10 by Notre Dame in the Cotton Bowl.

The man who buried Texas in that game was one of college football's unlikeliest-looking superstars. His name was Joe Montana, a gangly quarterback who seemed lost under his pads and helmet. He could not throw hard, and he could not throw far, and he was not even all that accurate. In fact, he had never exactly nailed down the starting job. But all season long, when the Fighting Irish were up against it, coach Dan Devine watched Montana bring his team back. Montana guided Notre Dame to the national championship with a perfect performance against the Longhorns, and was a preseason contender in 1978 for the Heisman Trophy. He blew his shot at the award when he played poorly in the year's first two contests, but then he caught fire and led the team to 9 wins in its next 10 games. The final victory came against the University of Houston in the Cotton Bowl, and it sealed Montana's reputation as football's miracle man. The Irish were down 34-12 with less than eight minutes to play, the wind was howling through the stadium at 30 miles per hour, and the wind chill factor made the temperature feel like six degrees. Montana engineered a wild comeback, tossing the decisive touchdown with no time remaining on the clock.

The other top college quarterbacks of the 1970s were also great field generals, though none had the luck to work with a team as good as Notre Dame. Jim Plunkett, Bert Jones, Steve Bartkowski, Tommy Kramer, and Marc Wilson each earned All-America recognition, but none even came close to challenging the top teams for the national title. Montana did have another advantage over these players: He seemed to understand the complex relationships formed by different offensive sets, different defenses, and the personnel in the game on each and every play. Only a few people really noticed, but he was playing a different brand of football than his rifle-armed contemporaries. Indeed, Montana's greatest influence would be exerted on the professional game in the 1980s. Not until the 1990s would college quarterbacks be asked to run a team the way Montana did.

Pro Football: After the Merger

As in most team sports, dramatic gains in offense are usually met with a swift response from the defense. This was certainly true in the NFL during the 1970s: Better passing created an army of pass-rushing specialists; a new bunch of 1,000-yard runners gave birth to a legion of mobile, gapplugging linebackers, and more complex passing strategies gave rise to a generation of fierce, hard-hitting pickoff artists. In the early years of the decade fans were very interested in how the old AFL franchises would do against the NFC clubs. By the end of the decade, no one even cared. The merger went more smoothly than anyone

had believed possible, and the bigger, better 24-team National Football League set course on a decade of superstars and super teams. Four franchises dominated the 1970s: the Dallas Cowboys, Miami Dolphins, Minnesota Vikings, and Pittsburgh Steelers. Three of these teams had been laughing stocks only a few years earlier, but shrewd trading, productive drafts, and smart coaching transformed them into extraordinarily balanced clubs. In the new NFL, that was the way it was supposed to be. There was plenty of talent, lots of money, and each week the league drew new fans by the thousands.

Dallas coach Tom Landry put together an awesome squad. He blended new recruits with players left over from the excellent Cowboy teams of the 1960s. Quarterback Don Meredith was replaced by his backup, Craig Morton, who was in turn replaced by Roger Staubach, who had fulfilled his four-year service requirement in the Navy. Morton led the team to the NFC championship game in 1970 and 1971, then gave way to Staubach, who took the team to the Super Bowl three more times. The running attack in the early part of the decade featured

The Dallas Cowboys, "America's Team," take the field with coach Tom Landry at the fore.

Calvin Hill, Duane Thomas, Walt Garrison, and Robert Newhouse. One way or another it was good for between 1,500 and 2,000 yards a year, which kept defenses busy stopping the run and not paying enough attention to the pass. For this, Dallas opponents paid dearly. In 1972, Morton led the NFL in touchdown passes, and Staubach did the same in 1973 and three more times in the late 1970s.

By then the offensive personnel had changed, with Newhouse and pass-catching veteran Preston Pearson joined by Tony Dorsett in the Dallas backfield. The Cowboys also added deep-threat wideouts Drew Pearson and Tony Hill, and tight end Billy Joe Dupree. This team, which won the NFC title in 1975, 1977, and 1978, was almost unstoppable. Containing the unpredictable Dorsett required the full attention of at least one linebacker, and kept pass rushers from going all-out except on the most obvious throwing downs. This gave Staubach the extra half-second he needed to find one of his glue-fingered receivers. When defenders did get through, Roger the Dodger usually managed to squirm away—either to complete a pass or pick up big yardage himself.

The Dallas defense was an excellent one throughout the decade. Harvey "Too Mean" Martin, the team's sack specialist, was at one end while Ed "Too Tall" Jones wreaked havoc on the other. Bob Lilly established himself as the greatest defensive tackle of his era, and by the time he retired he had passed that honor on to his protege, Randy White. White's savage play earned him the nickname "Manster"—half-man, half-monster. Among the other top Cowboys in the trenches during the 1970s were Jethro Pugh, Bill Gregory, and Larry Cole. The Dallas linebacking corps starred Lee Roy

Jordan, Chuck Howley, D. D. Lewis, Bob Bruenig, and Hollywood Henderson, while the defensive backfield was manned by Cliff Harris, Mel Renfro, and Charlie Waters, who also made things happen on special teams. In all, the Cowboys went to the Super Bowl four times during the decade, winning two and losing two.

Though a little less flashy, the Dolphins were remarkably similar to the Cowboys. A season after losing Super Bowl III to the Jets, coach Don Shula left the Colts to run the Miami team. He welcomed the opportunity to mold an exciting core of young talent—something he never had in Baltimore. Shula made the most of his opportunity, approaching his job with great skill and intelligence. In former Purdue University star Bob Griese, he knew he had a capable quarterback. In Larry Csonka, Jim Kiick, and Mercury Morris he had a group of runners that could grind out tough yards up the middle and break big plays around end. And in an offensive line led by budding superstar Larry Little and talented castoffs Jim Langer and Bob Kuchenberg, Shula had the kind of unit that could both protect Griese and create a bit of daylight for his running backs. A trade for veteran Paul Warfield—one of the top deep-threat receivers of the 1960s while with Cleveland—completed an offensive package that blossomed from the moment Shula assumed control of the team.

Shula had less to work with on defense, so he taught his players how to read and react as a single unit. Eventually, some stars did emerge from this system, including middle linebacker Nick Buoniconti, defensive tackle Manny Fernandez, and defensive backs Jake Scott and Dick Anderson. At a time when defensive units were nicknamed "Fearsome Foursome" and "Purple People

Miami running back Larry Csonka bulldozes his way into the end zone for the first touchdown of Super Bowl VIII. The Dolphins' victory over Minnesota was their second consecutive Super Bowl triumph.

Eaters," the Dolphins called themselves the "No-Name Defense." It was a loose bunch playing with no pressure, and in their first season under Shula they were a big reason why Miami improved from 3 wins in 1969 to 10 in 1970. In 1971, the Dolphins made the playoffs. They beat the Kansas City Chiefs in overtime, and shutout the Colts in the AFC title game to earn a Super Bowl berth. In this era before free agency, it was extremely unusual for a team to improve so dramatically with basically the same bunch of players.

What the Dolphins did in 1972, however, was totally unique. That season the No-Names allowed the fewest points in pro football, Csonka and Morris became the first teammates to rush for 1,000 yards each, and former soccer player Garo Yepremian booted 24 field goals to produce 14 victories in 14 games. The Dolphins defeated some of the top teams in football, including the Chiefs, Vikings, Jets, and Giants, and only three games all year were close. When Griese went down with an injury at mid-season, veteran backup Earl Morrall—the longtime sub for Johnny Unitas when Shula coached the Colts—stepped in and had an MVP season at the age of 38. The Dolphins pulled off a comeback win over the Browns in the playoffs, then beat the Steelers 21-17 in the AFC championship game when Griese returned to action. Against the Redskins in the Super Bowl the Dolphins dominated, giving up just one touchdown. When the final gun sounded, Shula and his players had gone through an entire season undefeated—something no other team has ever done.

The Dolphins reached the Super Bowl again the following year, beating the Minnesota Vikings. Throughout the 1970s, the Vikings were the team no one wanted to play. They had won the NFL title in 1969 and had been on the verge of building a dynasty when their quarterback and inspirational leader, Joe Kapp, refused to play without a big raise in 1970 and was shipped to the Patriots. The Vikings had a defense that featured a top player at virtually every position, and they specialized in performing in the brutal cold. The front line—or "Purple People Eaters"—boasted wily veteran Jim Marshall, 6'6"Carl Eller, and a spectacular defensive tackle named Alan Page. In 1971, Page beat his man consistently in every single game, wreaking so much havoc that he was awarded the league's MVP award. A unique player, he lined up slightly off the line, and hesitated just an instant after the ball was snapped so he could read the play. He could follow a ball carrier from sideline to sideline, and he regularly racked up 15 sacks a year. Not even Page & Co. could solve Minnesota's lack of a playmaking quarterback, so the team traded for Fran Tarkenton, who had been the franchise's first star so many years earlier.

Playing for so many bad teams, the scrambling Tarkenton had developed a reputation as a novelty act. But he had learned a lot about football during those years, and when he returned to the Vikings he found the kind of unit that could complement his skills perfectly. With coach Bud Grant, he

developed an offense that seamlessly mixed a rugged ground game with a surgical passing attack. In his first year with the Vikes, Tarkenton became the NFC's top-ranked passer. In 1973, the Vikings drafted University of Miami running back Chuck Foreman, completing a backfield that included two-time All-American Ed Marinaro and veterans Bill Brown and Dave Osborn. With tackle Ron Yary leading the charge, the Viking offense scored more points than any team in the NFL. Meanwhile, the defense continued to dominate, giving up the fewest points in the NFC. The Vikings won their division every year from 1973 to 1978, and went to the Super Bowl three times. They are remembered as "losers" because they could not win the Super Bowl. Conversely, the Oakland Raiders, who won 100 games during the 1970s, are remembered as big winners, even though they only made it to one Super Bowl.

The greatest team of the 1970s—and, many feel, the finest ever—was the Pittsburgh Steelers. At the start of the decade, the franchise ranked as the worst in NFL history. The team had not won anything since before World War II, and rarely contended for a division title past the first week in October. They made stupid trades and ill-advised draft choices, and with few exceptions their most promising players failed to develop, unless they ended up playing for another team. That began to change in 1969 when owner Art Rooney hired coach Chuck Noll. Noll drafted defensive linemen Joe Greene and L. C. Greenwood out of small southern schools, put veteran linebacker Andy Russell in charge of the defense, and began to build a unit that would soon be called the "Steel Curtain." The team went 1–13 in Noll's first season, giving them

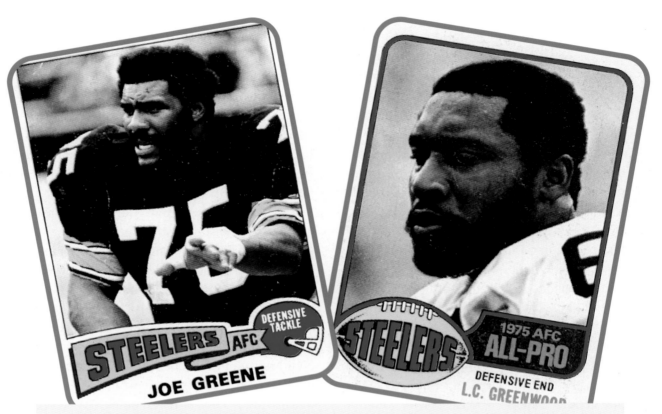

L. C. Greenwood and "Mean" Joe Greene, pictured here on trading cards, were but two of the many stars of Pittsburgh's feared "Steel Curtain" defense of the mid-1970s.

great position in the 1970 draft. The Steelers grabbed rifle-armed quarterback Terry Bradshaw and an enormous defensive back named Mel Blount, and finished the year with five wins. By 1972, the team had added more young defensive stars in Dwight White, Ernie Holmes, Jack Ham, and Mike Wagner. Unknown Roy Gerela had emerged as a top kicker and Bradshaw was starting to show signs of becoming a big-time quarterback. But the player who turned the Steelers into a football dynasty was running back Franco Harris.

Harris had received almost no attention at Penn State University, where he played beside all-purpose star Lydell Mitchell. Noll, however, saw in this unheralded full-

back just the man he needed: a sure-handed ball carrier who could hit a hole hard, but improvise if the hole was not there. Harris ignited the Steeler offense and energized Pittsburgh's working-class fans with his workmanlike performance. There was nothing fancy about Franco—he ate up yardage in the heat, the rain, and the snow—but at season's end he had piled up over 1,000 yards and led the league in yards per carry. Harris totally befuddled opposing defenses with his ability to come to a dead stop and then blast off in another direction. And he never, ever gave up on a play. That quality made him an NFL legend against the Oakland Raiders in the 1972 playoffs, when he plucked a deflected pass off his shoe tops with no time left on the clock and ran the ball into the end zone to win the game. Called the "Immaculate Reception," it remains the most disputed play in football history.

Noll continued to shape his team into a winner, taking the AFC central division crown year in and year out. Less a molder of men than a manipulator of players, he knew what it took to get the most out of each player and could be cruel and even dishonest if he felt that was what it would take. By 1974, the team had drafted a pair of great wide receivers in John Stallworth and Lynn Swann, and further shored up its defense with the addition of hard-hitting linebacker Jack Lambert, whose ability to play the pass was

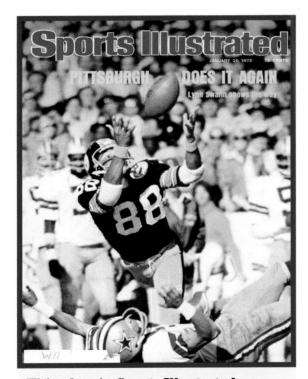

This classic *Sports Illustrated* cover summed up the excitement of receiver Lynn Swann's acrobatic catches in Super Bowl X.

nothing short of remarkable. These additions, plus the further maturation of the veterans, catapulted Pittsburgh to five AFC championship games in six years. The Steelers made it to four Super Bowls, winning each.

Outside of the quarterbacks for the Steelers, Vikings, Dolpins, and Cowboys, the only passer to come out of the 1970s with the recognition he deserved was probably Ken Stabler. Drafted by the Raiders in 1968, he languished on the bench for the better part of six seasons. Coach John Madden gave him the starting job in 1973, and Stabler rewarded him by completing a league-high 62.7 percent of his passes. In 1974, he led Oakland to the AFC title game and was named league MVP. Two seasons later he was the MVP again, and this time he passed the Raiders to a Super Bowl victory. Nicknamed "Snake" for the coolness with which he slithered away from pass rushers, Stabler took the lessons he learned from Bear Bryant in Alabama and applied them with great success in the pros. He took what the other teams gave him, and stole what they did not.

The finest runner of the 1970s, O. J. Simpson, never got a shot at the Super Bowl. In fact, the Buffalo Bills, who drafted him in 1969, rarely put a competitive team on the field. Yet despite the fact that opponents keyed on Simpson, he still managed to pile up an amazing amount of yardage. Simpson further sharpened the instincts he had developed at USC to become virtually uncatchable once he broke into the open. In 1973, Simpson's offensive line matured and he responded by becoming the first pro to crack the 2,000-yard barrier. His 1975 season was even better, as he amassed 1,817 yards on the ground and 428 more on 28 catches. The Bills asked him to pick up the tough, painful

O. J. Simpson running for daylight. Simpson was a terror in the open field and in 1973 became the first back to break the 2,000-yard mark.

yards, and he obliged. But at least once or twice a game he would burst through the defense for long, spectacular runs.

Simpson retired as the second-leading runner in NFL history to Jim Brown. The man who would eventually retire with that all-time record was Walter Payton, who broke in with the Chicago Bears in 1975. The "Monsters of the Midway" had been playing gruesome football for 10 years and, despite Payton's immense contributions, they would struggle to reach .500 for almost 10 more. During that time, Payton was the team's lone bright spot. A mix of speed, power, and attitude, the man they called "Sweetness" could leave a mighty sour taste in an opponent's mouth. On a trademark Payton run, he would squirt through the line or around end, put a move on a linebacker, and then accelerate and plow into a smaller defensive back. When he danced down the sideline, Payton made a point of not going out of bounds without a fight. He would use his rock-solid body as a battering ram to pick up an extra yard or two before he got shoved over the sideline, giving an opponent a little something to think about the next time they met. Amazingly, he missed just one game due to injury during his career despite playing with a horrible offensive line throughout the 1970s. More than just a runner, Payton was a superb blocker and a great pass-catching back. He even played quarterback when the Bears regular passers all got hurt.

College Football in the 1980s

As had been the case in every other era of college football, the athletes who took the field during the 1980s were a little bigger, a little stronger, and a little faster than their predecessors. Hard-core weight-training programs, scientifically engineered nutritional supplements, muscle-building drugs (legal and illegal), and performance-enhancing substances (mostly illegal) had started to show up in college locker rooms in the 1970s; by the 1980s they were even common in high schools. Colleges competed fiercely for the services of these teenage monsters, with the top-flight programs stocking their offensive and defensive lines two-deep if they could. In previous years a 220- or 230-pound player would have been a lineman, but many shifted into linebacker, tight-end, or fullback roles as 280-pound giants proliferated in the trenches.

THE BOYS OF SUMMER

By the end of the 1960s, professional football—fresh off the successful merger of the NFL and upstart AFL, and boasting skyhigh popularity and television revenues—was looking like a cash cow to investors. The temptation to try to duplicate the AFL's success was irresistible, and in 1973 the World Football League was formed. Its founder, Gary Davidson, had slapped together the World Hockey Association and it had managed to do all right; Davidson and his partners figured the success of another football league was practically guaranteed.

The WFL's twist was to start its games in July and play into the fall. It placed teams in NFL markets such as New York and Chicago and also established franchises in warm-weather cities that did not have professional football. The new league's plan was to build a fan base in these cities during 1974 by putting good football on the field, then rewarding the fans with a slew of NFL superstars signed to play in 1975 and 1976. By the time the first season got underway, NFL stars such as Ken Stabler, Calvin Hill, Daryl Lamonica, and the heart of the Miami Dolphin offense—Jim Kiick, Paul Warfield, and Larry Csonka—were all slated to join the league in a year's time.

After a fast start, however, the WFL began to collapse. Games were played at night on Wednesdays and Thursdays, and by midweek, most football fans had had their fill of the sport. Attendance plummeted, and all but two owners bailed out either during or after the first season. Still, the 1975 season would feature the NFL stars, and if a lucrative television contract could be negotiated it seemed the league would have a chance. But when the man the networks wanted—Joe Namath—turned down a $4 million offer, the dream died. Ten weeks into the 1975 season, the WFL officially went belly-up and its superstars were left with worthless contracts.

Another group of investors tried again in 1983, creating the United States Football League. The USFL played its games in the spring and summer, avoiding direct competition with the NFL for fans. The USFL did, however, offer enormous salaries to college stars, and managed to sign three straight Heisman Trophy winners—Herschel Walker, Mike Rozier, and Doug Flutie.

The USFL tested the NFL's commitment to acquiring and holding onto the best football talent, but the established league responded strongly. NFL teams ponied up big bucks for the best players, and after two seasons fans could tell that the USFL's talent was not even close to NFL standards. After struggling through a third season in 1985, the USFL decided to take on the NFL head-to-head by scheduling its 1986 games during the fall. The season never got off the ground, and the last gasp of the USFL took place in the courts, where the league failed to win a $1.69 billion lawsuit against the NFL.

The result, particularly for teams that couldn't recruit a slew of such behemoths for their offensive line, was that the ground game seemed to be reaching a state of "critical mass." Finding themselves unable to run the ball with any consistency, more and more college offenses turned to the passing game and began taking to the air.

College quarterbacks given this increased responsibility faced a tough challenge. To beat the size, speed, and sophistication of 1980s defenses, a quarterback had to learn to recognize complicated defensive alignments, bark out new plays at the line of scrimmage, and read coverage schemes that were often designed to lure them into making risky throws.

As the statistics show, they were ready to accept this challenge. The schoolboys of the 1970s grew up idolizing the great pro passers of the 1970s—Namath, Bradshaw, Staubach—so by the time they got to college their thinking was already quite sophisticated. In 1980, college quarterbacks connected on more than half their passes for the first time in history. As the decade progressed, that rate climbed over 55 percent. And by 1989 college teams were combining for an average of 400 passing yards per game—nearly 150 yards more than they had in the previous decade. Scoring also rose by nearly a touchdown a game during this period.

The cutting-edge passing programs of the 1980s included Brigham Young University and the University of Miami. Brigham Young was nothing short of a quarterback factory. After Marc Wilson set an NCAA record with 3,712 passing yards in 1979, Jim McMahon first brought BYU to national attention with a mix of skill and attitude. The flamboyantly rebellious Mc-

Mahon was an odd match with a religious university, but his passing arm was a perfect fit in the high-octane BYU offense. In 1980, he threw for 4,571 yards and 47 touchdowns to establish records that would last for nearly a decade. In 1983 the Cougars finished in the Top 10 for the first time in school history, as All-American senior Steve Young—a direct descendant of university founder Brigham Young—led the country with 306 completions, a 71.3 completion percentage, 3,802 yards, and 33 touchdown passes. The following year, with Robbie Bosco taking the snaps, the Cougars went 12–0 in the regular season. In the Holiday Bowl he overcame a severely sprained ankle to complete 30 of 42 passes and engineered three long drives to beat Michigan and win the national championship. By the end of the decade, other teams had caught up to Brigham Young, but the Cougars still had the nation's best passer in Ty Detmer, who threw for 4,560 yards as a sophomore in 1989 and then set the all-time mark with 5,188 yards in 1990.

Whereas Brigham Young often lacked balance between its offense and defense, Miami was able to blend great passing with all of the other things that keep a team at the top of the rankings. Under three coaches—Howard Schnellenberger, Jimmy Johnson, and Dennis Erickson—the Hurricanes went into a bowl game with a shot at the national championship no less than eight times between 1983 and 1992. Over those years Miami featured four great quarterbacks: big, mobile Jim Kelly, Bernie Kosar, Vinny Testaverde, and Steve Walsh. Kosar and Walsh led their teams to national championships, and when coach Erickson took the reins in 1989 Miami won another title. None of the Miami quarterbacks broke any passing records, but then again they did not need to—the team was stacked with talented running backs and receivers. Also some of the best college defensive linemen of the 1980s played for the 'Canes, including Lester Williams, Jerome Brown, Daniel Stubbs, Bill Hawkins, Greg Mark, Jimmie Jones, Russell Maryland, and Shane Curry. Backing them up were linebacking standouts Rod Carter and Maurice Crum, and defensive backs Selwyn Brown and Bennie Blades.

Challenging Miami for supremacy during the first half of the 1980s were the Nittany Lions of Penn State University. Coach Joe Paterno stuck with a ground attack, and further built on his well-deserved reputation for turning out big-time linebackers such as Ed Pyrts, Shane Conlan, and Scott Radecic. Three terrific backs handled the ball for Penn State: Curt Warner, Jon Williams, and D. J. Dozier. From 1980 to 1987, the team went 76–19–1, and won national titles in 1982 and 1986.

With almost every team throwing the football, it took quite a performance for a quarterback to stand out in the crowd. Dan Marino, John Elway, and Doug Flutie got the most attention in the early 1980s. Marino threw 31 TD passes in 1981 for the University of Pittsburgh, and established himself as one of the best collegiate dropback passers ever. Elway, whose father Jack coached the pass-happy program at San Diego State University, became the most publicized quarterback in the country despite playing for a lousy team at Stanford University. Elway could throw the ball a mile—across his body, on the run, off either foot—making him the most dangerous college passer in a generation. At 5'9" Doug Flutie of Boston College had neither the

arm strength nor the physical size of other quarterbacks, but he had a huge heart and the guts of a jewel thief. In 1984, he threw the most famous touchdown pass of the decade, finding roommate Gerard Phelan in the end zone with a 65-yard desperation fling that beat top-ranked Miami with no time left on the clock. That season he became the first college quarterback to amass more than 10,000 yards in a career, and he won the Heisman Trophy for his efforts.

Naturally, there were more top-flight receivers in college during the 1980s than ever before. Among the best were Cris Carter of Ohio State University, Tim Brown of Notre Dame University, Irving Fryar of

Boston College quarterback Doug Flutie squeaks out of trouble and delivers a pass during the 1984 Orange Bowl. Flutie's scrambling and passing eventually produced a miraculous last-second win for BC over Miami.

the University of Nebraska, and two-time All-American Anthony Carter of the University of Michigan. These players and many others developed pro-level skills during their college careers, and this would have an enormous impact on the NFL during the late 1980s and 1990s.

Even with teams running the ball nearly 20 percent less than they did during the mid-1970s, there were still great runners in college during the 1980s. Herschel Walker already had a linebacker's body and Olympic sprinter's speed while he was in high school, and he nearly won the Heisman Trophy when he gained 1,616 yards as a University of Georgia freshman in 1980. Behind his awesome running, the Bulldogs

Powerful Georgia running back Herschel Walker became a cover story many times over when he arrived on the college scene in 1980.

won the national title, and Walker earned All-America recognition for his efforts. He was even better his sophomore and junior years, becoming the first player in the 20th century to be an All-American his first three years, and he also won the Heisman Trophy in 1982. He skipped his senior season to join the USFL. Marcus Allen beat out Walker for the Heisman in 1981, as he set NCAA records with 2,432 yards and eight 200-yard games for the University of Southern California. A blocking fullback for Charles White early in his college career, Allen was a punishing runner with great moves who blossomed when he was moved to halfback in 1980. Totally shut out of the Heisman hardware was Eric Dickerson of Southern Methodist University, who gained a combined 3,000 yards during the 1981 and 1982 seasons. Dickerson was 6'2" and 220 pounds, and he had the kind of explosiveness needed to run inside. But what made him so exciting was that once he broke into the open he had the raw foot speed to outrun everyone on the field.

As the decade wore on, many other spectacularly talented runners captured the college football headlines. Mike Rozier of Nebraska won the 1983 Heisman Trophy as he led the nation with 2,148 yards, and brought the Cornhuskers to within a single point of a national championship. Bo Jackson of Auburn University, who won the 1985 Heisman, might have had the best combination of power and speed of any runner of his time. Oklahoma State University had a couple of gems in Thurman Thomas and Barry Sanders. Both were small by 1980s standards, but each had his own unique way of dominating play while on the field. Sanders, who led the nation in kick returns in 1987 while waiting for Thomas to graduate, had just one full year in the Cowboy backfield. But what a year it was: 344 carries, 2,628 yards, and a whopping 234 points on 39 touchdowns. And at the University of Florida a human bowling ball named Emmitt Smith seemed to gain six or eight yards time he touched the ball—even when he ran away from his blocking.

Although these great runners had that little something extra that enabled them to flourish in the land of the giants, they would need a little bit more to survive in the pros, where the tacklers were even bigger, even faster, and a whole lot smarter. But these backs, along with the quarterbacks and receivers of the day, earned their college laurels playing in complex, precise offenses that took many cues from the NFL—an experience that would allow them, and the defensive stars who played against them, to enter the draft more "NFL-ready" than ever before.

Pro Football in the 1980s

To most NFL fans, it seemed impossible that the great football of the 1970s would continue on into the 1980s. The game had been in perfect balance for so long, with all those terrific quarterbacks on one side of the ball and all of those defensive superstars on the other. In this respect, those fearful fans were correct. The decade would see offensive football become incredibly sophisticated, with the defenses struggling desperately to catch up. In the early 1980s, a new generation of quarterbacks came on the scene, already trained in the fine art of passing during their college years. Instead of having to sit on the bench and learn from the starter for three or four seasons, many of

these young passers were ready after just a few games. By the middle of the decade, passing and pass-receiving records were falling every year. And there were so many talented wide receivers available that many teams started lining up three on almost every play.

Naturally, defenses were altered to protect against the pass and to give the quarterback as little time as possible in the pocket. On the surface, this process was not very difficult. Football, after all, has always been a game that favored the defense—and for every top passer or receiver in the draft, there seemed to be a good defensive back. What made things especially rough for pro defenses was that there also were some great running backs coming into the league at the same time, and they already knew how to run against pass-oriented defenses. For this reason, players such as Earl Campbell, George Rogers, Joe Cribbs, Marcus Allen, Herschel Walker, and Eric Dickerson were even more dangerous in the pros than they had been in college. The problem of stopping the combination of great passing and great running was never really solved, but it did focus more attention than ever on linebackers, who were quite literally caught in the middle of this offensive revolution.

For years, linebackers had been there to stop the run, cover the occasional running back or tight end who ventured out for a short pass, and in general clog things up in the center of the field. In the 1980s, their position was under siege. The players they had had to stop in the past were not only better at what they did, they were now part of a bigger and much more sophisticated offensive plan. It became clear pretty quickly that the old three-man format would have to change to a four-man alignment, and that the position of middle linebacker would have to be greatly modified or eliminated. For most teams, a pair of "inside" linebackers were entrusted with stopping plays through the line and covering receivers coming out of the backfield. Another pair of "outside" linebackers were responsible for sideline-to-sideline pursuit, and on passing downs they either dropped back into short coverage or made an all-out rush at the quarterback. Many of the smaller, more mobile athletes who lined up at defensive end during previous decades were ideally suited for this role, because it enabled a player to line up almost anywhere and do almost anything.

Although the most successful teams of the 1980s—the Raiders, Redskins, Bears, and 49ers—had wonderful offensive units, what distinguished them from their rivals was that their defenses did keep pace with the offensive changes occurring in the sport. The Raiders, for example, had Marcus Allen, veteran quarterback Jim Plunkett, and receivers Todd Christiansen and Cliff Branch. But what propelled them to two AFC championships was a tough, opportunistic defense that often bent but ultimately refused to break. Defensive end Howie Long took charge of the line, stuffing the run and sacking the quarterback despite constant double-teaming. Lester Hayes led a group of pirates in the defensive backfield, and the team had a couple of on-the-edge big-play linebackers in Rod Martin and veteran Ted Hendricks. The Raiders used this formula to win two NFL titles, beating the Philadelphia Eagles in Super Bowl XV in 1980 and Washington Redskins in Super Bowl XVIII in 1983 despite coming into each game as a slight underdog.

The Redskins had won the Super Bowl a year earlier despite being lightly regarded when the 1982 season began. The team scored more than expected, thanks to the accuracy of quarterback Joe Theisman, the marvelous up-the-middle power of fullback John Riggins, and a near-perfect season from kicker Mark Moseley. But the defense was what kept them in so many tight ball games. Coach Joe Gibbs created a unit that was every bit as complex as the offenses it had to stop, relying on a number of veteran role-players and young stars such as defensive end Dexter Manley and linebacker Rich Milot. They held the Dolphins to 176 total yards in the Super Bowl and shut them out in the second half for Washington's first championship in almost 40 years. The 'Skins returned to the Super Bowl after winning the 1987 NFC championship, doing it the same way as always, with their hard-blocking "Hogs" on the offensive line, some clutch quarterbacking by veteran Doug Williams, and control of the line of scrimmage by defensive standouts Manley and Charles Mann.

The Bears won just one Super Bowl, but of all the teams of the 1980s their 1985 squad was perhaps the most dominant. For most of the season, in fact, it looked like Chicago might become the first team ever to go undefeated in a 16-game campaign. With 1,551 rushing yards and 49 catches, veteran Walter Payton was the team's best offensive weapon, but not its biggest. That honor went to William "The Refrigerator" Perry, a 6'2" rookie defensive tackle who tipped the scales somewhere in the neighborhood of 350 pounds, and who occasionally lined up next to Payton in the Bear backfield on short-yardage downs. Jim McMahon quarterbacked the team to 15 victories, and found plenty of time to irritate everyone

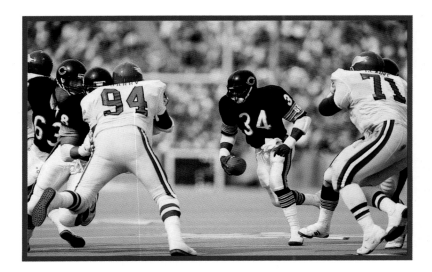

Walter Payton, the NFL's all-time leader in career rushing yards, looking for a hole to run through. "Sweetness" labored for mediocre Chicago teams for years before leading the Bears to their nearly perfect championship year of 1985.

from NFL commissioner Pete Rozelle to coach Mike Ditka. The Bears rolled through the playoffs and destroyed the New England Patriots in the Super Bowl.

Payton, Perry, and McMahon drew all of the media attention, yet it was defensive coordinator Buddy Ryan's unit that made life especially miserable for Chicago's opponents. The defensive line featured superstars Dan Hampton, Steve McMichael, and Richard Dent, who specialized in getting to the quarterback. The main beneficiary of this constant pressure was the Bear secondary, which picked off 23 passes. Veteran Gary Fencik had a career year, playing great pass defense and leading the team in tackles, and Wilber Marshall and Otis Wilson emerged as star linebackers. But it was the man in the middle, Mike Singletary, who made the defense go. Though just six feet tall, he made up with intelligence and intensity what he lacked in physical size. Singletary was as good against the run as anyone who ever played the position—and could hold his own in coverage, too. However, it was his ability to read the field and be in the

right place at the right time that gave the Bears such a huge edge.

When the decade was all said and done, the "Team of the Eighties" turned out to be the San Francisco 49ers. They brought together all of pro football's most important forces and added a few wrinkles of their own. Joe Montana, whose heroics at Notre Dame had caught the eye of coach Bill Walsh, sat on the bench during his 1979 rookie season, but was handed the starting quarterback job midway through the 1980 campaign. He responded by completing a team-record 65 percent of his passes and putting in motion an offense Walsh had been dreaming up since his days as an assistant with the Bengals and Chargers in the 1970s. To Walsh's thinking, a team that controlled the ball with short passes had an advantage over a running team because it made defensive players do things they were not used to doing. The 49ers often sent five men out on one play, so there was almost always someone open.

Montana was the perfect quarterback for this offense. He could freeze linebackers

With his San Francisco 49ers leading San Diego 48-10 at halftime in this 1988 game, coach Bill Walsh still finds reason to tinker on the blackboard with his high-powered offense.

with a ball fake, and scramble around until one of his teammates cut into the open. If he saw his opponents laying back for a pass, he would change the play at the line and send a runner through a weak spot in the defense. Montana worked hard in practice with his receivers and blockers until he knew where everyone would be on every play. This dedication paid off in 1981, when he became the league's top-ranked passer and San Francisco had the best record in football. In the NFC championship game, Montana engineered a 90-yard drive with just five minutes left to beat the Cowboys and advance to the Super Bowl. He threw the winning pass, just as he was getting buried by the Dallas pass rush, to a place he knew tight

end Dwight Clark had to be. In the Super Bowl against the Cincinnati Bengals, he opened up a 20-0 halftime lead and cruised to a 26-21 victory.

Forgotten in Montana's magical season is the fact that the 49er defense made crucial plays to seal both victories, including a magnificent goal-line stand to prevent the Bengals from scoring a go-ahead touchdown. Veteran linebacker Hacksaw Reynolds and pass-rushing specialist Fred Dean led a young, aggressive unit that starred rookie sensation Ronnie Lott. An All-American cornerback at the University of Southern California, Lott was the hardest hitting cornerback in more than a decade. And when opposing quarterbacks tested him in coverage he made them regret it, intercepting seven passes and converting three turnovers into San Francisco touchdowns. His running mate, safety Dwight Hicks, picked off nine passes and ran in two for scores.

Walsh realized he was onto something special, but was frustrated because—with the exception of Montana and Lott—the 49ers were basically a collection of ordinary players. So Walsh set about the task of drafting and trading for players he believed could be extraordinary. Over the next five years, he built an offensive line featuring big, smart players such as Randy Cross, Harris Barton, Bubba Paris, Guy McIntyre, and Jesse Sapolu. In the second round of the 1985 draft he selected an unheralded Nebraska University fullback named Roger Craig, and taught him how to catch passes out of the backfield. From the Tampa Bay Buccaneers he acquired quarterback Steve Young, who became the best backup passer in league history. In the 1986 draft, Walsh swapped picks with the Patriots and took Jerry Rice of Mississippi Valley State, another very special offensive player everyone else "missed." Walsh had discovered Rice in a highlight show while flipping through TV channels late one night, and jotted down the young man's name. By the early 1990s, Rice was being hailed as the greatest receiver in history. In the third round of the 1987 draft, Walsh grabbed Delaware State University end John Taylor, who at one time believed he had a better shot at making it as a professional bowler.

Walsh also made some brilliant defensive additions. Pass rusher Pierce Holt came from lightly regarded Angelo State College in Texas, and run-stopper Michael Carter was selected in the fifth round of the 1984

Future Hall-of-Famers Joe Montana and Jerry Rice take a look around the Louisiana Superdome before the 1990 Super Bowl.

draft. Linebacker Charles Haley was a fourth-round pick in 1986, and cornerback Tim McKyer was a third-rounder out of the University of Texas at Arlington. Each of these players contributed significantly to the team's success in the latter half of the 1980s, when San Francisco won the NFC's western division title six straight years. In two of those seasons—1988 and 1989—they returned to the Super Bowl, edging the Bengals in one game and blowing out the Broncos in the other. After his third NFL championship, Montana was being hailed as the greatest quarterback since Johnny Unitas. No one, it was said, saw the field like "Super Joe," and no one had ever mastered such a multifaceted offense.

Fans in Miami, however, were quick to claim their quarterback was history's best. Dan Marino had been selected by the Dol-

Miami quarterback Dan Marino hunts for a receiver. Marino's strong arm and quick release have brought him both the NFL's single-season and career passing-yardage marks.

phins with the 27th pick of the 1983 draft. The team had won the AFC championship the season before and thus had a very low spot in the draft. Coach Don Shula could hardly believe his good fortune when the University of Pittsburgh star was still available. There were several other top college passers available that year and Marino's health and off-field habits had come into question, so he slipped to the bottom of the first round. When starter David Woodley failed to inspire the Miami offense early in the season, Shula inserted Marino and he responded by connected for 20 touchdowns in just 11 games.

Pro football had never seen anything quite like Marino. He had developed a lightning-quick release that enabled him to catch sagging defenses off-guard, and a feathery touch that let him lay the ball out for a receiver who had only a step or two on his man. If defenses tried to take away the short and medium stuff, Marino had the arm strength and accuracy to burn them deep. And even when the coverage was perfect, he could still hit his receivers with hard, pinpoint passes. As a rookie, he drew comparisons to a young and healthy Joe Namath—his knack for releasing the ball before a receiver actually broke into the clear was reminiscent of the former New York Jets star. Indeed, Marino would sometimes ignore an open man and throw the ball to a teammate who was about to get open if he thought that man had a better chance to score.

To say Marino caught the league by surprise would be a major understatement. He was so quick, so deceptive—so much better than anyone believed possible—that in his first full season he obliterated the old NFL marks with 362 completions, 5,084 passing yards, and 48 touchdowns. Marino led Miami to the AFC's best record, connecting with favorite receivers Mark Duper and Mark Clayton 144 times. The team's defense was nothing to brag about, but members of the secondary made big plays when they had to in all but a couple of games. Unfortunately, one of those games was the Super Bowl. In what was correctly billed as a showdown between the NFL's two young superstars, Marino and Joe Montana hooked up in an exhibition of precision passing. The game turned on Miami's poor punting, as well as Montana's ability to exploit the inexperience of the Dolphin linebacker crew. Miami fans took some consolation in the fact that, as the team matured, they would likely return to the Super Bowl many times. As it turned out, the Dolphin defense struggled the rest of the decade and Marino never made it back to the big game.

For this very reason, Denver fans felt that they had the game's best quarterback. John Elway entered the league the same year as Marino, and he too raised eyebrows with his NFL-ready passing skills. But unlike Marino, after seven seasons he had taken the Broncos to three Super Bowls. More mobile than Marino, and possessing a stronger arm, Elway could turn a busted play into a 30-yard gain. And in do-or-die situations, he was at his most dangerous.

Among the top NFL runners of the 1980s were a couple of fellows who were already household names from their college days. Earl Campbell continued to pile-drive tacklers with the Houston Oilers, where he starred for six seasons. In 1978, he won Rookie of the Year and MVP honors, and came within an eyelash of breaking O. J. Simpson's league rushing mark in 1980. In all, the "Texas Rose" led the AFC in rushing four consecutive years, and was pretty much the entire Oiler offense until 1984, when he was traded to the Saints. The man who did break O.J.'s mark was Eric Dickerson, who was drafted by the Los Angeles Rams in 1983. The team had a decent passing game and good blocking, giving Dickerson an ideal situation in which to strut his stuff. In his second season, he ran for 2,105 yards to set a new record. He reached the 10,000-yard plateau faster than anyone in

Houston's Earl Campbell was about as easy to tackle as a freight train, as this photograph amply demonstrates.

history, but a 1988 trade to the Colts doomed his career. The team had no offensive options other than Dickerson, and he absorbed a tremendous amount of punishment. His skills declined quickly, as did his enthusiasm for the game and by 1990 he was a mere shadow of his former self.

With the role of linebackers evolving throughout the decade, it was difficult for teams to create a good unit, and almost impossible to keep it together for more than a year or two. The exception to this rule was the New York Giants, whose overwhelming defense flowed from the play of its linebacking corps. In Harry Carson, the Giants had the first great inside linebacker. Time and again he read and reacted to inside penetration, often "hitting the hole" at the same time as the man with the ball. Carson was big, mean, and intense—a combination that

enabled him to shed 300-pound tackles and dominate play on the inside. This freed up teammate Lawrence Taylor to do what he did best: annihilate anything that moved. Taylor, New York's top outside man, was the greatest pass-rushing linebacker ever to play. He could not be stopped one-on-one, and no one ever knew where he would line up or what he would do next. Taylor could singlehandedly destroy an offense because of this unpredictability. Initially the Giants (like most teams of the time) called set defensive plays that required Taylor to be in a certain place performing a specific function. But it became clear early on that the best way to use him was to simply unleash him. Taylor could fight off a block with one arm and make a tackle with the other. He could hurdle a 6'5" opponent and land on the quarterback. He could chase a play from

Fierce and blazingly fast, Giants linebacker Lawrence Taylor was every NFL quarterback's worst nightmare. Here he blindsides Tampa Bay's Craig Erickson in 1993.

one side of the field to the other, and he could slip through the line before anyone could get a body on him. An All-Pro in his first 10 seasons, in 1986 Taylor became the second defensive player ever to be named NFL MVP. Carson and Taylor were made all the more effective by the team's other top linebackers, including Gary Reasons, Byron Hunt, Andy Headen, Carl Banks, Pepper Johnson, and Steve DeOssie. And this group, in turn, was made even better by coach Bill Parcells, a former linebacking coach who was promoted to head coach in 1983. With quarterbacks Phil Simms and Jeff Hostetler handling the offense, Parcells was able to guide his linebacker-rich team to Super Bowl victories twice in a five-year span.

The premier pass-rushers of the 1980s were Mark Gastineau and Reggie White. Gastineau was the star of the New York "Sack Exchange," the Jets defensive unit that included Marty Lyons, Joe Klecko, Abdul Salaam, Lance Mehl, and Greg Buttle. Gastineau stood 6'6" and was as quick as any defensive end in football. And he went crazy every time he buried a quarterback, dancing around in the backfield and whipping up the crowd. It got so bad that the league had to pass a rule outlawing "celebrating." In the latter half of the decade, Reggie White of the Philadelphia Eagles was the NFL's sack master. White was as big as the guards and tackles he faced and much, much faster. Despite constant double-teaming, he led the league in sacks in 1987 and 1988, and was the only player in the 1980s (and 1990s for that matter) who averaged more than one sack per game. No defensive end has ever used the combination of quickness and strength as well as White. If a blocker tried to beat him to a

Mark Gastineau celebrates a sack of Miami quarterback Dave Woodley in 1983. Gastineau was the leader of the Jets' "New York Sack Exchange" defensive line.

spot, he would wait until his man was slightly off-balance and then push him aside. If an opponent chose to stand his ground, White would make a move and charge right past him.

As the decade closed on the NFL, financial issues were on the minds of players, owners, and fans. Throughout the 1980s television ratings had been slipping, and the league tinkered with the regular-season and playoff schedules to increase fan interest. The new TV deal signed in 1987 still generated millions for each team but was not as lucrative as the 1981 agreement. With salaries on the rise, a lot of owners were worried about what the 1990s would bring.

THE MAN WHO MADE THINGS HAPPEN

When the Oakland Raiders hired 34-year-old Al Davis to be their general manager and head coach in 1963, they wanted someone who could bring a new attitude to the team. He scrapped Oakland's dreary uniforms, replacing them with jerseys of silver and black, and helped design a nasty new logo. Davis drilled into his players the concept of "Pride and Poise," and within a year the Raiders were the roughest, toughest, scariest team in the American Football League. In 1966, Davis was named AFL commissioner, and he immediately started encouraging his owners to sign the NFL's top players to future contracts. This strategy helped bring about the NFL-AFL merger. It was an agreement Davis never liked. He believed that the AFL was about to surpass the NFL in terms of big-name stars and quality of play, and he was further irritated when he was passed over for the commissioner's job in the new merged league. He returned to the Raiders as managing general partner, and began a long feud with NFL commissioner Pete Rozelle.

This conflict came to a head in 1980, when the city of Oakland refused to build income-producing luxury boxes for the Raiders' stadium. Meanwhile, the Rams had left the Los Angeles Coliseum and started playing their games in nearby Anaheim. Davis, feeling the Rams had abandoned the L.A. market, signed an agreement with the Coliseum to transfer his team there. Such a move required the okay of Davis's fellow owners, which he never sought. When Rozelle blocked the Raider move, Davis took the NFL to court, claiming that as long as no one's territorial rights were being violated, Rozelle had no right to say where a team could or could not play. Prior to the 1982 season a judge ruled in favor of Davis, awarding the Raiders $35 million and allowing them to move to Los Angeles. The lawsuit sent a message to the NFL that it was not invincible, and paved the way toward other franchise moves during the next two decades.

A young Al Davis on the sidelines with his Oakland Raiders in 1963. Davis himself designed the Raiders' silver-and-black uniforms.

They had good reason. In 1989, the NFL Players Association forced the league to adopt a limited free-agency plan, and commissioner Pete Rozelle—the guiding light of football for nearly 30 years—announced his retirement.

College Football in the 1990s

Prior to the University of Miami's 31-30 victory over the Nebraska Cornhuskers in the 1984 Orange Bowl, no Florida college football team had ever claimed a national championship. During the 1990s, three Florida universities—Miami, Florida State, and Florida—won it all. Their dominance on the college football scene during the 1990s was such that, on any given weekend, a football fan was more likely than not to see one of these three schools atop the NCAA rankings.

Dennis Erickson's Hurricanes could not repeat their 1989 national championship in 1990, but did reclaim the top spot in 1991. The team almost won again in 1992, but lost the national title to the University of Alabama 34-13 in the Orange Bowl. Quarterback Gino Torretta won the 1992 Heisman and grabbed most of the headlines, yet it was the Hurricane defense that kept Miami within striking distance even when the offense was not clicking.

Florida rose to prominence in 1994 and won the national championship in 1996 behind the pass-oriented offense of coach Steve Spurrier and the strong arms of Terry Dean and Danny Wuerffel. They split the job in 1993 and again in 1994, when each finished among the Top Five in the NCAA quarterback ratings and the Gators held the top spot until mid-October. By 1996, Wuerffel was in charge, and the team's offense averaged more than 500 yards per game. He led the nation with 39 touchdown passes, and threw for over 3,500 yards. The Gators destroyed arch nemesis Florida State 52-20 in the Sugar Bowl to win the national title, and Wuerffel won the Heisman Trophy.

Florida State's 1996 Sugar Bowl loss to Florida was a rare low point in a decade that otherwise saw the Seminoles sustain a remarkably high level of success. Prior to that, coach Bobby Bowden had guided his Seminoles to 11 straight bowl game victories. Florida State won its first national championship in 1993, edging Nebraska 18-16 in the Orange Bowl, and the school was ranked in the Top 10 each year during the 1990s. The trademark of Bowden's teams was defense. The Seminoles boasted several consensus All-Americans, including linebackers Marvin Jones and Derrick Brooks, linemen Pete Boulware and Reinard Wilson, and defensive backs Terrell Buckley, Corey Sawyer, and Clifton Abraham. The most-talked-about Seminole, however, was quarterback Charlie Ward. A bright, daring passer and great scrambler who could sniff out a scoring opportunity, Ward established himself as college football's strongest leader, and one of history's finest big-play quarterbacks. He joined Torretta and Wuerffel in winning a Heisman while playing for a Florida school.

Challenging all three Florida teams for supremacy in the mid-1990s was the University of Nebraska. The Cornhuskers had had a strong team for decades, and an unbroken string of bowl appearances dating back to the 1960s. But during the years 1993 to 1995, coach Tom Osborne's squad was easily the best in college football. The

THE STRIKE

In the summer of 1982, the players and the league sat down to discuss a new labor agreement. The owners were content to continue on with the same basic contract. The NFL Players Association countered with a plan that would change the face of sports. They wanted to become business partners, asking for a share of the cash the owners were raking in. The players believed that they were entitled to 55 percent of team revenues. The owners refused, and the players walked out for two months. It was not until mid-November that a new agreement was reached and the season resumed. Although the radical profit-sharing proposal was not adopted, it did sow the seeds for future labor negotiations in a number of sports and led to many of the ideas behind the salary-cap agreements that were worked out in the 1990s.

In 1987, football's labor agreement had to be renewed again, and the two sides still found themselves at odds on a number of issues. The players walked out as they had five years earlier, but this time the owners were ready. They continued the NFL schedule with "replacement" players, and the games counted in the standings. The fans and the media hated this solution, as did several high-salaried stars, who were losing $100,000 and more per week. When some of football's biggest names began crossing the picket line, the union gave in and the players went back to work.

As these "replacement fans" show, the 1987 NFL players' strike and the owners' use of replacement players was an embarrassment to everyone connected to pro football.

quarterback during this period was Tommie Frazier, who in 1992 became the first freshman QB to start during Osborne's long tenure. A fine passer and devastating runner, Frazier worked with running backs Calvin Jones and Lawrence Phillips to thoroughly befuddle their Big Eight foes. With a front line led by Zach Wiegert, Lance Lundberg, and Brenden Stai, the 'Huskers rolled over opponents all season long in 1993, but lost the national championship to Florida State on a missed field goal. In 1994, the Cornhuskers returned with a more seasoned Frazier and a much improved Phillips, who ran for more than 1,700 yards in his sophomore year. Nebraska met Miami in the Orange

Bowl with the national championship on the line, and fell behind 17-7 in the third quarter. But Frazier made several huge plays and fullback Cory Schlesinger broke off a pair of touchdown runs to give Nebraska a 24-17 victory. In 1995 the Cornhuskers were at it again, moving ahead of Florida State in the polls at mid-season and holding onto that lead right to the end. Frazier was magnificent in his senior season, earning All-America honors. Phillips, on the other hand, was suspended for disciplinary reasons and played only five games. Still, the Cornhusker machine was just unstoppable, as second-ranked Florida discovered in the Fiesta Bowl. In a game that placed an exclamation point on one of the great runs in Big Eight history, Nebraska put a major hurt on the Gators with a 62-24 win.

Although Frazier earned most of the accolades in the Big Eight, he might not have been the conference's best quarterback.

In a 1993 game between Notre Dame and Florida State, quarterback Charlie Ward steps into a pass just ahead of a hit from Jim Flanigan of the Fighting Irish.

Many felt that honor belonged to Kordell Stewart of the University of Colorado. He was a remarkable athlete with a special flair for dramatics. Stewart combined a tremendous arm with terrific running ability and drove defenses crazy. In 1993 he threw for 2,299 yards and rushed for 524 more. In 1994 Stewart teamed with wide receiver Michael Westbrook and running back Rashaan Salaam to challenge for the national championship, but a loss to undefeated Nebraska denied them a shot at the top spot. Salaam, a junior, was the star of the 1994 team, gaining over 2,000 yards and winning the Heisman Trophy. The highlight of the season, however, involved Stewart and Westbrook. In a September game against powerful Michigan, Stewart heaved the ball 75 yards in the air with time expiring and the Wolverines up by six points. When the ball came down, Westbrook plucked it out of the air for one of the most spectacular finishes in football history.

Salaam declared himself eligible for the NFL draft after his fantastic junior year, denying himself a chance at becoming the top college runner of the 1990s. Had he stayed at Colorado he surely would have drawn comparisons to Marshall Faulk, who tore it up for San Diego State University from 1991 to 1993. Faulk earned All-America honors and was in contention for the Heisman in each of those seasons. He became the first freshman to lead the NCAA in points scored and yards gained per game. Faulk tied Emmitt Smith's record when he cracked the 1,000-yard mark in only his seventh college contest, and he and Herschel Walker are the only players to surpass 3,000 career yards as sophomores. Faulk had the power to blow through a hole, the explosiveness to turn the corner, and the pure speed to pull away from tacklers once he hit the open field. He could also run routes and catch passes, making him a threat to score on almost every play.

Two of the most intriguing college players during the 1990s could not have been more different from each other. Peyton Manning was the classic drop-back quarterback, running a pro-type offense for the University of Tennessee. The son of former NFL star Archie Manning, he grew up surrounded by money, fame, and football. By the time he was in high school, Manning

Tennessee quarterback Peyton Manning, son of NFL star Archie Manning, seems to be a sure thing to follow his father into the ranks of successful pro quarterbacks. Here he unloads in a 1997 game against Kentucky.

probably knew more about what it takes to be a successful big-time quarterback than most big-time quarterbacks. He exhibited pro-level skills as a college sophomore, when he led the Volunteers to national prominence. As a junior, he improved his arm strength, footwork, size, and speed, and by season's end he was virtually guaranteed of becoming the first pick in the NFL draft. There was just one problem: he wanted to stay in college. Manning enjoyed being the big man on campus. He liked going to parties with other students, he loved taking classes, and there was nothing like the excitement that built up around the school in anticipation of a big game. Manning knew that once he left college he would never be in a situation like that again. And he also felt there was still some room for improvement. So Manning passed up millions, returned to school in the fall of 1997 and enrolled in graduate-level classes. The choice thrilled fans of the Volunteers, who watched as Manning had led Tennessee to the SEC championship and a berth in the Orange Bowl. Manning was edged out by Michigan cornerback Charles Woodson in Heisman Trophy voting, but became only the fourth football player to win the Sullivan Award, honoring the nation's top amateur athlete.

Steve McNair grew up an underdog, far from the limelight. He played a little QB in high school, but it was for his promise as a defensive back that tiny Alcorn State University offered him a scholarship in 1991. McNair accepted, and then quietly set his sights on becoming the team's quarterback. His powerful arm and great running—as well as his knack for making things happen—convinced the Braves coaching staff to give him the starting job as a freshman.

McNair responded by becoming the most dynamic player in college football. He was the Southwest Athletic Conference Player of the Year in each of his four seasons, and by the end of his senior year he had generated more total yards of offense than any college player in history. "Air McNair" even gained unanimous All-America honors, which is virtually unheard of for a player from a small Division I-AA school. As the 1995 NFL draft approached, a great debate raged over McNair's qualifications. He had exhibited quite clearly that he could make plays under pressure. His arm, legs, and head were unquestionably of pro caliber. In fact, even as a rookie he would probably have more raw talent than almost every other NFL quarterback. What worried people about McNair is that he had been playing in an offensive system that was built around his incredible mobility and his quick-strike capabilities. Could he learn to be a more conservative quarterback and run a more complex NFL offense? Could he accept conforming to a rigid system, when in the past the system had always conformed to him? These questions were being asked about a lot of supertalented college quarterbacks during the 1990s, including Kordell Stewart and Charlie Ward. Ward, in fact, was not even drafted—despite winning the Heisman Trophy! Luckily, he had another option—basketball. Moving from field general to floor general, he became a point guard for the NBA's New York Knicks.

Others were not so fortunate. Players like Tommie Frazier were viewed by NFL coaches as round pegs that would not fit in the square hole that, in many ways, is an excellent description of the pro quarterback position. Instead, most mobile college quarterbacks were drafted and asked to play safety or cornerback. They were asked to draw on their physical abilities and knowledge of the passing game to compete for spots with lifelong DBs. Not surprisingly, few made it. Meanwhile, quarterbacks such as Manning, who was fortunate to play in pro-style offenses, are drafted without hesitation—even if their skills and athleticism are rated lower.

For many Americans, the question is not whether you like football but how far you'll go to express your love of the game.

As the 1990s draw to a close, the debate still rages. Colleges that build offenses around game-breaking athletes such as McNair and Frazier often achieve great success, but—given the rigidity of most NFL offenses—doing so virtually assures that these multitalented quarterbacks will not have an NFL career. Should colleges run a pro-style system in order to recruit top high-school quarterbacks and help them make it in the NFL? Or should NFL teams take the risk of radically redesigning their offenses to make the most of the talents of today's star players? In any case, the relationship between the NFL and college games is only going to get more complicated until the NFL begins to change.

Pro Football in the 1990s

Of all the major North American sports leagues, none has proved to be more focused on establishing and achieving specific goals than the National Football League. After suffering through two work stoppages, shrinking interest, and a disappointing television deal during the 1980s, commissioner Paul Tagliabue and the league set a course to remedy these ills and take professional football to a new level of public interest and awareness. The first task was to iron out a labor agreement with the players. In 1992, federal judge David Doty ruled that the "Plan B" free agency system, in place since 1989, was illegal. Doty drove home his point by granting several stars immediate free agency. The huge salaries they commanded on the open market—tight end Keith Jackson, in particular—opened a lot of eyes on both sides.

The players realized that, as a group, they were being significantly underpaid. The owners realized that the demand for good players might soon drive up salaries by close to 100 percent. Both sides recognized that a new agreement would have to be hammered out.

Throughout the 1992 season the players and the owners struggled to find common ground, yet when each made its "best offer" they were still miles apart. With a new television deal being negotiated and the marketing arm of the NFL undergoing significant changes, a work stoppage would have been disastrous. Judge Doty stepped in again, threatening to come up with a solution himself if the players and the league did not. The thought of a football outsider determining their future was so terrifying that a new deal was announced a day later. Among other things, it stated that a player would become a free agent after five years in the league, and players finishing the third and fourth years of their contracts might also get a chance to test the free-agent waters. Also, the spring draft was reduced to eight rounds, allowing more college players to shop their services to the teams that needed them. In return the players agreed to work under a salary cap, giving the owners what they most wanted: a clear picture of what it would cost to run their football teams. Both sides agreed to follow these rules until 1999, when football's financial picture would be re-evaluated and adjustments made. With labor peace assured, commissioner Tagliabue was able to negotiate a television deal that paid the league nearly $4.5 billion. This generated more income for the teams and a higher salary cap for the players. Another move that benefited both the owners and players was the addition of expansion franchises in Jacksonville, Florida; and Charlotte, North Carolina; for the 1995 season.

To improve its product on the field the NFL made several changes in its rules during the 1990s, most of which were designed to increase the number of touchdowns scored. Kickoffs were moved back to the 30-yard line; after missed field goals the other team got the ball from the point of the miss; and defensive backs were prohibited from hitting receivers after they had gone more than five yards from the line of scrimmage. In 1994, two-point conversions were used for the first time in league history, giving teams a chance to make eight points from a touchdown. This further reduced the benefits of trying for field goals, which had fallen out of favor in 1993 when more three-pointers were attempted and made than ever before. The new rules did what they were supposed to, increasing offense and generating excitement. The new free agency also worked as planned, helping mediocre franchises fill their needs with established stars and generating renewed fan interest in those cities.

During the 1990s, the marquee team of the league was once again the Dallas Cowboys, which also helped the NFL. After the team collapsed in the 1980s oil baron Jerry Jones bought the Cowboys, dumped longtime coach Tom Landry, and installed his old college roomate Jimmy Johnson as the team's new head man. Johnson had succeeded Howard Schnellenberger at the University of Miami in 1984 and coached the team to a national championship. He brought the same enthusiasm and decisiveness to the Cowboys, who had amassed quite a number of young players. Under

Johnson the team went 1–15 in 1989, but rebounded quickly and became a playoff contender by 1991.

Johnson had a top passer in Troy Aikman, who came out of UCLA as the number one quarterback in the country. He also had receiver Michael Irvin, one of his favorite players from Miami. Five games into his first season, Johnson traded the team's top runner, Herschel Walker, to the Minnesota Vikings for first- and second-round picks in the next three drafts. In 1990, he used one of those picks to select running back Emmitt Smith, who decided against playing his senior season for the University of Florida. He used five more choices on tackle Erik Williams, center Mark Stepnoski, defensive linemen Russell Maryland and Leon Lett, and linebacker Ken Norton. Johnson kept the good

Emmitt Smith of the Dallas Cowboys has been one of the most productive running backs of the 1990s—not least because he has huge linemen like Nate Newton (61) to open holes for him.

players he inherited from Landry—including defensive standouts Tony Cassillas, Jack Del Rio, and Bill Bates—and began to mold them into one of the best teams in NFL history.

The Cowboys won the 1992 NFC title and destroyed the Buffalo Bills 52-17 in Super Bowl XXVII, then returned to the big game a year later and beat the Bills 30-13. Two years later Dallas was back in the Super Bowl (this time under new coach Barry Switzer) and Aikman and company disposed of the Pittsburgh Steelers with relative ease for a third NFL championship. The Aikman-Smith-Irvin combination gave the Cowboys as good a three-man offense as any team has ever had. The key man was Smith, who ranks as one of the great possession backs in history. Quick, strong, and courageous, he had a special talent for picking up a couple of extra yards as he was being tackled. Smith could also catch a pass and pick his way through the defense for big gains. His greatest talent, however, was his vision. Somehow, he always knew where the hole would be, even if it was not there when he took a handoff. Needless to say, this gave him an incredible advantage, because as a rule defensive players do not move to plug holes that have not yet opened. With blocking fullback Daryl Johnston clearing a path for Smith, it was difficult to keep him from piling up big yards—one year he averaged over five per carry. He was the Dallas workhorse during the team's glory years, leading the league in rushing four times and touchdowns three times between 1991 and 1995.

Smith carried the ball 20 to 25 times a game and was particularly adept at eating up precious minutes when the Cowboys were protecting a lead. Those leads were usually created by the skilled passing of Aikman. He had an excellent arm, he set up smoothly, and he was very good at reading coverage. He could throw from the pocket or deliver the ball on the run, and there was never any question who the Dallas field leader was. Aikman used his weapons intelligently and with great skill, hitting Smith and Johnston in stride with flair passes, throwing long and strong to wideouts Alvin Harper and Kevin Williams, drilling crisp passes to tight end Jay Novacek, and hitting Irvin with every type of pass in the Dallas playbook. Irvin was one of those once-in-a-lifetime receivers that most quarterbacks can only dream of having on their teams. At 6'2" and 200-plus pounds, Irvin could take whatever a defensive back could dish out and give it right back. His big hands, deceptive speed, and tremendous jumping skill meant he could out-reach most opponents for a high pass, and his ability to adjust to balls that were not thrown well made him an excellent possession receiver. An ultracompetitive athlete with incredible confidence, he regularly hauled in half a dozen passes a game despite constant double-coverage.

During the 1990s, the San Francisco 49ers did not reach the Super Bowl until the 1994 season. From 1988 to 1994, however, they were in the NFC championship game six times. Bill Walsh left the team in 1989 to coach at Stanford University and was replaced by George Seifert, who guided the team to a Super Bowl victory in his very first year. But the "Team of the Eighties" was getting old in the 1990s, and although the 49ers still had great players, they needed to blend new personnel into the mix before they were able to return to the Super Bowl. Much of the transition focused on the status of injured veteran Joe Montana, who missed the entire 1991 season and played just once in 1992.

Montana's replacement, longtime sub Steve Young, finally got a chance to shine at the age of 30 and he responded by becoming the highest-rated quarterback in the league. In 1992, he threw for 25 touchdowns and completed two-thirds of his passes to win the MVP award. Young repeated as the NFL's top player two seasons later when he had 35 TDs and completed 70.3 percent of his passes. Besides possessing a magnificent arm, Young had the size, speed, and instincts of a fullback. He used both of these talents with devastating effectiveness, galloping downfield for huge gains when his receivers were covered, and throwing the football all over the field when

Steve Young of the 49ers barks out signals during a 1996 playoff game. Young had to wait in the wings for years as Joe Montana's backup, but when he finally got his chance he became an all-pro.

they were not. Like Montana, he was able to think right along with his teammates, and he was every bit as good a medium-range passer. Yet despite breaking most of Montana's records during the 1990s, Young was in his predecessor's shadow until he finally led the team past the Cowboys in 1994 and into Super Bowl XXIX, where the 49ers beat the San Diego Chargers 49-26.

San Francisco added some important new players during the 1990s, including running backs Ricky Watters and William Floyd, defensive back Merton Hanks, and defensive tackles Bryant Young and Dana Stubblefield. Left over from the Montana years were tight end Brent Jones, wideouts Jerry Rice and John Taylor, and offensive linemen Jesse Sapolu, Harris Barton, and Steve Wallace. The team also attracted several veteran free agents, who signed on with the 49ers for less money than they were offered elsewhere because they wanted a shot at a Super Bowl. This enabled San Francisco to put valuable players such as Richard Dent, Bart Oates, Tim McDonald, Ken Norton, Ray Brown, and Deion Sanders on the field and still operate under the salary cap.

So good were the 49ers during the 1990s that, despite their lack of Super Bowl victories, their coaching assistants were in great demand throughout the league. Offensive coordinator Mike Holmgren, for example, accepted the seemingly thankless head-coaching position with the Green Bay Packers and did a wonderful job. He took with him the 49er offense and swiped benchwarmer Brett Favre from the Atlanta Falcons to run it for him. Within a couple of seasons, Green Bay had returned to the top of the pile in the NFL and Favre was voted MVP three years in a row. Favre was a mon-

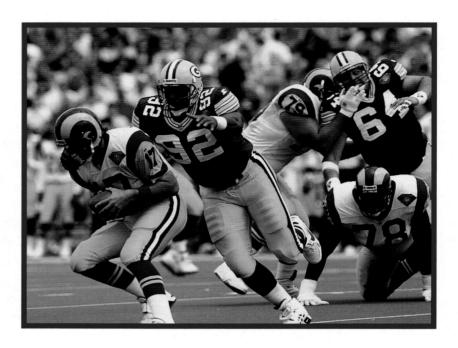

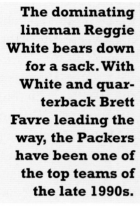

The dominating lineman Reggie White bears down for a sack. With White and quarterback Brett Favre leading the way, the Packers have been one of the top teams of the late 1990s.

strously talented quarterback who had never been taught that it took 22 guys to win a football game. When Holmgren convinced him that his job was to run the offense and not try to bring the crowd to its feet with miracle passes, the Packers surpassed the Cowboys as the team to beat in the NFC. The Green Bay defense was anchored by Reggie White, the most celebrated of the NFL's free-agent class in 1993. He signed with the Packers in part because he saw in young stars such as Favre, Edgar Bennett, and Robert Brooks the makings of a good offense. And in linebackers George Koonce and Wayne Simmons and linemate Gilbert Brown, White recognized a young defense on the rise. In four seasons the Packers were Super Bowl champions.

In the AFC, the Buffalo Bills established themselves as the team to beat during the 1990s, winning the eastern division six times between 1988 and 1995. Jim Kelly proved a highly capable quarterback during these years, providing great leadership and

a strong right arm. Running duties were handled by Thurman Thomas, who gained more than 1,000 yards every season from 1989 to 1996. The receiving corps featured such sure-handed veterans as James Lofton, Andre Reed, Don Beebe, and Bill Brooks. The defense was led by pass rusher Bruce Smith, linebacker Cornelius Bennett, and safety Henry Jones.

Although the team would have gone nowhere without Kelly in command, Thomas and Smith were the ones who enabled the Bills to crush their opponents. The 5'10" Thomas did everything well, despite having ordinary speed and moves for a man his size. Sometimes it seemed he made plays on heart alone, and he always seemed strongest at the end of games, when the Bills most desperately needed him. Smith was a monster when he entered the league in 1986, and he worked to stay in shape as he got older. The result was a career that saw him in a neck-and-neck battle with Reggie White as the NFL's best all-around

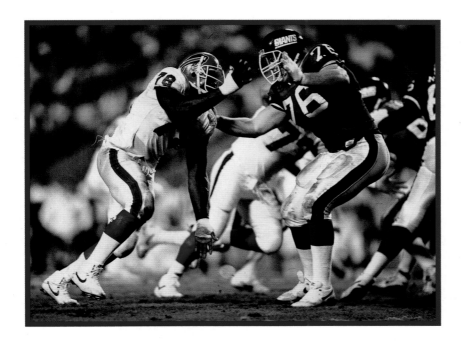

In a duel of all-pros, Buffalo defensive end Bruce Smith tries to beat Giants tackle Jumbo Elliot during Super Bowl XXV.

defensive lineman—a battle a lot of people would say Smith won. So quick and so big was Smith that he could explode in one direction, then shove his blocker in that same direction while simultaneously cutting the opposite way and blowing past him. Although Buffalo reached the Super Bowl a record four consecutive times during the 1990s, the team lost each game. Like the Vikings of the 1970s, the Bills of the 1990s may go down in history as "losers," even though they were the only AFC team from 1990 to 1997 that managed to hold a halftime lead during an eight-year run of Super Bowl dominance by the NFC.

Aside from Emmitt Smith and Thurman Thomas, there was only one other running back in the 1990s who could pick up a team and carry it to victory. That was Thomas's old teammate at Oklahoma State, Barry Sanders. Drafted by the Detroit Lions after his junior year, Sanders proved that big things can sometimes come in very small packages. Playing for a mediocre team in a sometimes bizarre offensive system, he averaged about 100 yards a game throughout the 1990s and led the NFL in rushing four times. He had his greatest year in 1997, strapping the Lions on his back and carrying them to the playoffs and amassing the second-highest single-season rushing total—2,053 yards— in league history. The numbers, however, do not even hint at the kind of back he was. Whenever Sanders got the ball, he was a threat to score. He would twist, spin, stutter-step, reverse field—anything he could to avoid being tackled. If Sanders darted into a hole and it started to close up, he would take a couple of steps back and go somewhere else looking for a little daylight. When he found it, he was the fastest player in the league over 10 or 15 yards. Sanders was the man defensive players hated to face, because he could make the same guy look bad 10 times in the same game. Sanders was often compared to Gale Sayers, and some claimed that he could make his moves even quicker than the Chicago Bear Hall of Famer.

The lack of superstar runners during the 1990s hit the fullback spot hardest of all. On most running plays, the fullback was used as a decoy or a blocker for the halfback. On passing plays, many teams took the fullback out of the game, replacing him with a receiver or pass-catching back. And when teams passed on first and second downs, they generally kept the fullback in as part of the pass protection. Also, halfbacks were being asked to pick up a lot of the hard up-the-middle yards that had previously gone to the fullbacks.

The main beneficiaries of this shift in strategy were the wide receivers. More plays were being run for receivers and more balls were coming their way. Prior to 1990, only two receivers had ever caught 100 passes in a season. From 1990 to 1997, 13 different players reached the 100-catch plateau a total of 20 times.

If the 1990s are remembered for anything, it will be for the marvelous pass-catchers who helped revolutionize the game. Among the "super receivers" of the decade were wideouts Sterling Sharpe, Cris Carter, Tim Brown, Herman Moore, Carl Pickens, and Jerry Rice, as well as tight ends Ben Coates and Shannon Sharpe.

The leader of this pack, of course, was Rice. The right man in the right place—with the right people throwing to him—Rice combined good fortune with an incredible package of receiving skills to smash just about every record in the book. He had the raw speed to flash by a defender and grab a long bomb, but he could also take a short pass and turn it into a 30- or 40-yard gain. In fact, he actually worked on this skill during practice, grabbing 12-yard tosses, making a move on an imaginary tackler and then sprinting all the way to the end zone. When the 49ers

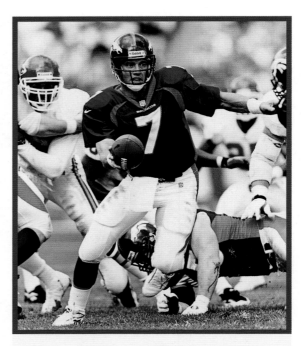

Quarterback John Elway capped a brilliant career by guiding his Denver Broncos to a long-awaited Super Bowl victory in 1998.

needed a clutch grab Rice was also the man they chose, for he rarely dropped a pass and could absorb a big hit without losing the football. Everything that coaches look for in a receiver Rice had. He came off the line quickly, he ran his patterns with grace and precision, he had tremendous hands and leaping ability, and when the ball was in the air he could generate a little extra speed. From 1990 to 1996 (Rice was injured in 1997), he averaged 100 catches a year, and led the league in receiving yards five times.

Needless to say, quarterbacks got an awful lot of attention during the 1990s. Besides Young, Favre, and Aikman, old pros John Elway and Dan Marino continued to make headlines. Each fought off injuries during the 1990s and endured the ups and downs of their respective teams. Marino's skills remained high, but his 1993 season was destroyed by an Achilles tendon injury. In 1994 Marino returned to form and the Dolphins looked like a cinch to get to the AFC title. But a last-minute loss to the underdog San Diego Chargers in the playoffs robbed Marino of his best chance at another Super Bowl since he first made it a decade earlier.

The 1997 season would be John Elway's 15th in the NFL, and over the years he had treated fans to numerous last-gasp heroics and racked up all the honors and accolades a football player could hope for, save one—a Super Bowl ring. He'd taken his Broncos to the big game three times in the late 1980s and come away each time on the losing end of lopsided blowouts. But this season would be different. Behind Elway's leadership and the bruising running of halfback Terrell Davis, the Broncos made it back to the Super Bowl and—to nearly everyone's astonishment—beat the defending-champ Green Bay Packers in one of the few real nail-biters the NFL's showcase game has seen in recent years.

By the end of the 1990s, a lot of familiar faces will have left the NFL. In fact, the top players nearing the twilight years of their careers could occupy their own wing in the Hall of Fame. The final decade of the 20th century provided a stage for some of the finest players in history, and set the tone for football's future. As great as today's players are, the past tells us that even greater players are probably just on the horizon. Yes, it is tempting to say that there will never be another Dan Marino, but fans of Sammy Baugh, Johnny Unitas, and Joe Montana thought their guy was the ultimate quarterback. It is hard to imagine that a runner like Barry Sanders will ever come into the league again, but somewhere out there is a halfback who is an inch shorter, a step faster, and even more of a nightmare to tackle. And even though Jerry Rice is putting up seemingly untouchable numbers, some coach flipping the television dial at this very moment may be stopping to watch a highlight tape of the man who will come along and smash all of his records. That is the beauty of football. It is in a constant state of evolution, if for no other reason than because the human mind, body, and spirit are constantly changing for the better. Best of all, history shows that change can come from anywhere at any time—from a grizzled veteran working on the move that will help him squeeze another year out of his career, to a crazy kid on a muddy field dreaming of a 100-yard field goal.

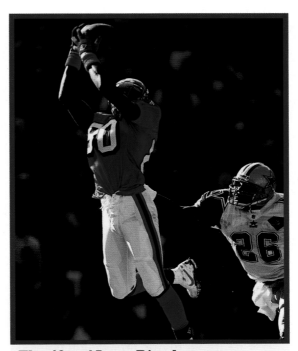

The 49ers' Jerry Rice has never stopped reaching for the seemingly impossible; here he rises for a touchdown grab against the arch-rival Cowboys.

A Football Timeline

1869 COLLEGE—Princeton and Rutgers play the first intercollegiate game. The field used by most schools is 120 yards long by 75 yards wide, with goal posts 24 feet apart. All goals count as one point.

1875 COLLEGE—Several schools adopt the egg-shaped, leather-covered rugby ball.

1876 COLLEGE—The field width is set at its present 53 ⅓ yards. Team size is reduced from 20 to 15 players.

1880 COLLEGE—Team size is reduced to present 11-man squad. The line of scrimmage is established.

1882 COLLEGE—The modern system of downs is instituted. In order to keep track of the yards needed to make a first down, chalk lines are added to the field, five yards apart.

1883 COLLEGE—The scoring rules are changed, with touchdowns counting as four points and field goals as five.

1888 COLLEGE—Yale completes history's first perfect season, winning all 13 of its games without giving up a single point.

1889 COLLEGE—Walter Camp chooses the first All-America team. Amos Alonzo Stagg, Pudge Heffelfinger, and Edgar Allen Poe—nephew of the great poet—are among the inaugural selectees.

1892 PRO—Former Yale star Pudge Heffelfinger accepts a one-game fee of $500 from the Allegheny Athletic Club, becoming the first professional player.

1895 PRO—John Brallier of Latrobe is the first openly paid professional.

1897 COLLEGE—Touchdowns are increased in value to six points.

1899 PRO—The Morgan Athletic Club fields a football team on Chicago's South Side. The team is the direct ancestor of the Arizona Cardinals, making it the oldest continuous operation in pro football.

1902 COLLEGE—Michigan beats Stanford 49-0 in what is regarded as the first Rose Bowl.

1904 COLLEGE—Field goals are reduced in value to four points.

PRO—Charles Follis of Ohio's Shelby Athletic Club becomes the first African-American professional football player.

1906 COLLEGE—The flying wedge and other mass plays are ruled illegal, while the forward pass is legalized in both college and the pros. Yards needed to make a first down are increased from five to ten.

1909 Field goals are reduced from four points to three in both the college and pro game.

1910 COLLEGE—In an attempt to curtail mass play, seven offensive players are required to be on the line of scrimmage when the ball is snapped.

1912 COLLEGE—Official field shortened by 10 yards to 100, but 10-yard end zones are added.

PRO—Touchdowns are increased from five points to six.

1914 COLLEGE—A "roughing the passer" rule is instituted. Washington and Oregon State play to a scoreless tie, ending Washington's 39-game winning streak. The school goes 24 more games before actually losing.

1916 PRO—Jim Thorpe leads the Canton Bulldogs to the pro football championship.

1919 PRO—The Green Bay Packers begin play, sponsored by the Indian Packing Company.

1920 PRO—The American Professional Football Association is formed, with Jim Thorpe installed as its figurehead president. Thirteen teams compete in the league, which does not have an official schedule. The Akron Pros are awarded the league championship.

1921 COLLEGE—Undefeated teams meet in the Rose Bowl for the first time, as California beats Ohio State 28-0.

PRO—Joe Carr is named APFA president. The APFA plays its first organized season, and the Chicago Staleys win the championship with a 10–1–1 record. Fritz Pollard of the Akron Pros becomes the first African-American head coach in pro football.

1922 COLLEGE—Undefeated California meets undefeated Washington & Jefferson in the Rose Bowl, and the two team keep their records clean, playing to a scoreless tie.

PRO—The APFA changes its name to the National Football League (NFL). Owner George Halas changes the name of the Chicago Staleys to the Bears. Jim Thorpe and other Native American players form a team called the Indians, which is sponsored by the Oorang Kennel. The players put on performances in war bonnets, and trained dogs perform the halftime show. Guy Chamberlain's Canton Bulldogs win the league title.

1923 PRO—The Canton Bulldogs play their 25th straight game without a defeat.

1924 COLLEGE—John Heisman accepts the coaching job at Rice, his eighth school in 32 seasons.

1925 COLLEGE—The first East-West Shrine Bowl is played, marking the beginning of college football's oldest postseason all-star game.

PRO—The NFL begins using a lined ball, which holds its shape better during games. Red Grange quits school after his final game and signs with the Chicago Bears, drawing unprecedented national attention to the NFL. Sports promoter C. C. Pyle arranges two long tours for Grange and the Bears—the first against NFL teams and eastern All-Star squads, the second against All-Star teams in the south and west. The Pottsville Maroons fashion the league's best record, but play an unauthorized All-Star game in Philadelphia, violating the territorial rights of the Frankford Yellow Jackets. As punishment, the NFL awards the championship to the Chicago Cardinals.

1926 PRO—Red Grange and manager C. C. Pyle form the American Football League after they are refused an NFL franchise. The NFL, hoping to maintain good relations with college coaches, passes a rule forbidding the signing of a player before his class graduates. The Milwaukee Badgers are forced out of the league after using four high-school players in a game against the Chicago Cardinals. Ernie Nevers signs with the Duluth Eskimos and embarks on a 29-game tour. He kicks five field goals in a 15-0 win, and completes 17 straight passes in another victory.

1927 COLLEGE—Goal posts are moved to rear of the end zone. Notre Dame defeats Southern California at Soldier Field in Chicago in front of an estimated 120,000 fans.

PRO—The NFL dumps 12 franchises and adds 2 new ones prior to the season. Red Grange, playing with the New York Yankees, destroys his knee in a game against his old team, the Chicago Bears.

1929 PRO—Ernie Nevers scores all 40 points for the Chicago Cardinals in a 40-6 win over the Chicago Bears.

1930 PRO—The New York Giants beat a team of former Notre Dame players coached by Knute Rockne in a charity game before 55,000 fans. The game generates much-needed prestige and publicity for the NFL.

1931 COLLEGE—Notre Dame coach Knute Rockne dies in a plane crash. His teams won 88.1 percent of their games, which remains the best coach's winning percentage in college history.

1932 COLLEGE—Several rules are put into effect in order to increase safety, including a ban on flying tackles and blocks, and penalties for striking an opponent above the shoulders. Notre Dame completes its 41st consecutive winning season.

PRO—The NFL shrinks to eight teams, as the Great Depression takes its toll on attendance.

1933 COLLEGE—Players are urged to wear leather helmets, although many refuse to comply.

PRO—The NFL begins using a modern football, which is much easier to pass but extremely difficult to drop-kick. Hashmarks are added to the field, passing becomes legal from anywhere behind the line of scrimmage, and the goal posts are moved to the goal line. The Chicago Bears defeat the New York Giants 23-21 in the NFL's first official championship game.

1934 COLLEGE—Several rules and the shape of ball are altered to encourage more passing.

PRO—The football is reduced slightly in size, arriving at the exact specifications used to this day. Chicago halfback Beattie Feathers becomes pro football's first 1,000-yard rusher. The New York Giants beat the Bears 30-13 on an icy field to win the NFL title. The Giants play the second half in sneakers to get extra traction, and score 27 points in the final quarter.

1935 COLLEGE—The first Orange and Sugar Bowl games are played. Jay Berwanger of the University of Chicago wins the first Heisman Trophy.

PRO—The NFL initiates its first college draft. Green Bay Packer rookie Don Hutson catches his first pass and runs it into the end zone for an 83-yard TD. The Detroit Lions win the NFL championship in only their second year.

1936 COLLEGE—Jay Berwanger decides not to play in the NFL and enters private business. The Associated Press begins publishing national rankings. Minnesota (7–1–0) is selected as AP's first national champion. No team has ever been the national champion more than twice in a row.

PRO—A new pro organization, the American Football League, begins its first of two unsuccessful seasons.

1937 COLLEGE—The first Cotton Bowl game is played. Whizzer White of Colorado becomes the first collegiate 1,000-yard rusher. The Maxwell and Walter Camp Awards are established, each honoring the nation's top player.

PRO—The Boston Redskins move to Washington, D.C. The NFL adds a new franchise, the Cleveland Rams.

1938 COLLEGE—The Duke defense becomes the first team in football's passing era to go through an entire season without giving up a single point.

1939 COLLEGE—Use of helmets becomes mandatory.

PRO—NFL attendance tops the one million mark for the first time.

1940 COLLEGE—Tom Harmon of Michigan becomes the first player to finish his college career with more than 2,000 rushing yards.

PRO—Sammy Baugh of the

Washington Redskins averages a record 50.4 yards per punt. Quarterback Sid Luckman leads the Chicago Bears to a 73-0 defeat of the Washington Redskins in the NFL championship game. A new pro league is formed, again taking the name American Football League.

1941 COLLEGE—White balls come into use for night games. Platooning comes into use when substitution rules are greatly relaxed.

PRO—Former Notre Dame star Elmer Layden is named NFL commissioner. The AFL folds after just two seasons.

1942 COLLEGE—Frank Sinkwich of Georgia becomes the first player to run and pass for more than 2,000 yards.

PRO—Don Hutson catches 17 touchdown passes, establishing a record that still stands.

1943 COLLEGE—Notre Dame beats Michigan in the first meeting between the first-ranked team and the second ranked-team since weekly ratings have been published.

PRO—World War II decimates NFL rosters, causing the Cleveland Rams to suspend operations for a year. Several retired stars return to action, including Bronko Nagurski, who helps the Bears win the western division title. And free substitution rules are adopted so that older players do not have to play entire games. Sid Luckman throws seven touchdowns in a game held on "Sid Luckman Day."

1944 COLLEGE—Curt Kuykendall of Auburn becomes the first football player to rush for more than 300 yards in a game. Army averages 56 points per game, establishing an all-time record.

PRO—Coaching from the sidelines is legalized, allowing coaches to send plays into the huddle with signals or substitutes.

1945 COLLEGE—Forward passing is legalized from anywhere behind the line, encouraging use of modern T formation and enhancing the role of the quarterback. Glenn Davis of Army averages 11.5 yards per carry to set a record that stands to this day. His teammate, Doc Blanchard, becomes the first fullback to win the Heisman Trophy.

1946 COLLEGE—The first Gator Bowl game is played, with Wake Forest beating South Carolina. Bobby Layne of Texas runs, throws, catches, and kicks for 40 points in a 40-27 win over Missouri in the Cotton Bowl. Amos Alonzo Stagg coaches his 548th and final game. Army's Glenn Davis wins the Heisman Trophy after finishing second in the voting the two previous seasons. The Outland Trophy is established to honor the nation's top lineman. Notre Dame's George Connor is the first winner.

PRO—Elmer Layden retires as NFL commissioner and is replaced by Bert Bell. The All-American Football Conference (AAFC) begins play. Kenny Washington, Woody Strode, Marion Motley, and Bill Willis become the first blacks to play in the NFL since 1933. The free substitution rule is amended to limit a team to three players at a time. A game-fixing scandal rocks the NFL.

1948 **COLLEGE**—Bennie Oosterbaan takes over as coach of Michigan and leads team to national championship.

PRO—Several members of the Los Angeles Rams paint yellow horns on their helmets, marking the first appearance of helmet emblems in the NFL. Charlie Conerley of the New York Giants sets a rookie record with 22 touchdown passes.

1949 **COLLEGE**—SMU's Doak Walker is named MVP of the Cotton Bowl after winning the Heisman Trophy a few weeks earlier. Blockers are no longer allowed to grab with their hands.

PRO—Free substitutions return to the NFL on a trial basis. Steve Van Buren of the Philadelphia Eagles becomes history's first two-time 1,000-yard rusher. The Eagles win their second straight NFL championship and record their second consecutive title game shutout. The Cleveland Browns win their fourth AAFC

championship in a row. The AAFC merges with the NFL.

1950 **PRO**—The New York Giants play a preseason contest against the CFL's Ottawa Rough Riders, marking the first international football game. The free substitution rule is officially adopted by the NFL, opening the door to the age of specialization. Tom Fears of the Los Angeles Rams catches a record 18 passes in one game. The Cleveland Browns score a 30-28 comeback win over the Los Angeles Rams to win the NFL championship.

1951 **PRO**—Norm Van Brocklin of the Los Angeles Rams throws for 554 yards in a game. Elroy Hirsch of the Rams ties Don Hutson's record with 17 touchdown catches. The NFL championship game is televised coast-to-coast for the first time. The American Conference beats the National Conference 28-27 in the first NFL Pro Bowl game.

1952 **COLLEGE**—Al Brosky of Illinois intercepts a pass in a record 15th consecutive game.

PRO—The Pittsburgh Steelers become the last team to abandon the old single-wing formation, adopting the modern T-formation which is run by the quarterback. Night Train Lane, a rookie walk-on with the Los Angeles Rams, intercepts a record 14 passes.

1953 **COLLEGE**—Substitution rules are

tightened to prevent offensive and defensive platoons, but these rules are gradually relaxed over the next decade.

1954   PRO—The NFL passes a rule that all players must wear face masks, but veterans are allowed to play without them. Joe Perry of the San Francisco 49ers records the first back-to-back 1,000-yard seasons. Cleveland quarterback Otto Graham runs for three touchdowns and passes for three more as the Browns defeat the Detroit Lions 56-10 in the NFL championship game.

1955   COLLEGE—Art Luppino of Arizona becomes the first back-to-back college rushing champion.

PRO—The Los Angeles Rams and New York Giants play the NFL's first sudden-death overtime game during the preseason. The Cleveland Browns win their division for the 10th consecutive season.

1956   PRO—The NFL Players Association is formed.

1957   COLLEGE—Oklahoma wins its 47th game in a row, establishing an all-time record.

PRO—A record regular-season crowd of 102,368 attends a game between the Los Angeles Rams and San Francisco 49ers. Lou Groza of the Cleveland Browns leads the NFL in field goals for a record fifth time. Jim Brown of the Browns leads the NFL in rushing

and wins the first MVP award in his rookie season.

1958   PRO—Jim Brown of the Cleveland Browns becomes the first runner to gain more than 1,500 yards in a season. The Baltimore Colts defeat the New York Giants 23-17 for the league title in the NFL's first official sudden-death overtime game.

1959   COLLEGE—The distance between the goal posts is widened by nearly five feet, causing the total number of field goals to jump from 103 to 199 in one season.

PRO—The American Football League (AFL) is formed, with plans to begin play in 1960. Former South Dakota governor Joe Foss is named commissioner. Johnny Unitas of the Baltimore Colts becomes the first player to throw more than 30 touchdown passes in a season.

1960   PRO—Los Angeles Rams general manager Pete Rozelle is named NFL commissioner. Johnny Unitas of the Baltimore Colts throws a TD pass in a record 47th consecutive game. Halfback/kicker Paul Hornung of the Green Bay Packers scores a record 176 points. The Philadelphia Eagles beat the Packers 17-13 to win the NFL title. The Eagles are led by quarterback Norm Van Brocklin and center/linebacker Chuck Bednarik, each playing in his final pro game. George Blanda passes for three touchdowns and kicks a field goal and three extra points to lead the Houston Oilers to a 24-16 victory over the Los Angeles Chargers in the first AFL championship game.

1961 PRO—Lionel Taylor of the AFL Denver Broncos becomes the first professional receiver to catch 100 passes in a season. Combined NFL and AFL attendance tops the five million mark. Canton, Ohio, is selected as the site for the Pro Football Hall of Fame.

1962 COLLEGE—All players are urged by the NCAA to wear mouth protectors.

PRO—The AFL plays its first All-Star game.

1963 COLLEGE—Southern California beats Wisconsin in the Rose Bowl, marking the first time the top two teams in the country meet in a bowl game.

PRO—Superstars Paul Hornung and Alex Karras are suspended for a year for betting on pro football games. Jim Brown gains 1,863 yards and wins his sixth of eight career rushing titles.

1964 PRO—The AFL signs a five-year television deal with NBC for $36 million, giving the league the financial stability it needs to survive a war with the NFL. CBS pays twice that amount to broadcast NFL games. Pete Gogolak of the Buffalo Bills becomes pro football's first

soccer-style place kicker. Charley Hennigan of the Houston Oilers catches 101 passes and becomes the first receiver to top 1,500 receiving yards. Gary Collins catches three TD passes as the Cleveland Browns defeat the Baltimore Colts in the NFL championship game.

1965 COLLEGE—Tulsa receiver Howard Twilley averages 13.4 catches and 177.9 receiving yards per game, establishing a record that stands to this day.

PRO—The penalty flags used by referees are changed from white to bright yellow. Gale Sayers of the Chicago Bears sets a record for rookies with 22 touchdowns. Lenny Moore of the Baltimore Colts scores a touchdown in a record 18th straight game. A Harris Poll reveals that football surpasses baseball as the nation's favorite spectator sport.

1966 PRO—The Atlanta Falcons become the first new NFL franchise since World War II. Buddy Young is named NFL Director of Player Relations, making him the first African-American to work in the commissioner's office. The NFL and AFL hold secret merger discussions after the leagues spend $7 million signing their draft choices. They agree to form one league, but play separate schedules until 1970. The Super Bowl is created as the new pro championship game.

1967 PRO—Bubba Smith is the first player selected in the first combined NFL-AFL draft. Jim Bakken of the St. Louis Cardinals kicks seven field goals in a game. Travis Williams of the Green Bay Packers averages a record 41.1 yards per kickoff return. The Packers beat the Kansas City Chiefs in the first Super Bowl. Emlen Tunnell of the 1956 champion Giants becomes the first African-American player elected to the Hall of Fame.

1968 COLLEGE—Greg Cook of Cincinnati becomes the first college quarterback to throw for more than 500 yards in a game.

PRO—The New Orleans Saints become the NFL's second expansion team. The Houston Oilers move into the Astrodome, becoming the first pro team to play its home games indoors. Football fans on the East Coast find themselves watching the movie *Heidi* when NBC switches away from a Jets-Raiders game with a minute to go, causing millions of viewers to miss a remarkable comeback by the Raiders. The Green Bay Packers repeat as Super Bowl champions, defeating the Oakland Raiders. George Halas retires as coach of the Chicago Bears—a position he held on and off since the franchise was began operation a half-century earlier.

1969 PRO—Joe Namath leads the AFL's New York Jets to a Super Bowl victory over the heavily favored Baltimore Colts. The Baltimore Colts, Cleveland Browns, and Pittsburgh Steelers agree to move to the American Football Conference when the two leagues officially merge into the NFL in 1970.

1970 COLLEGE—Stanford's Jim Plunkett becomes the first college quarterback to amass 7,500 career passing yards.

PRO—The NFL is split into the American Conference and National Conference, with three divisions in each. The three division winners in each conference qualify for the playoffs along with one "wild card" team in each conference. All players wear names on their jerseys for the first time. The Cleveland Browns beat the New York Jets in the first Monday Night Football broadcast. Fred Cox of the Minnesota Vikings kicks a field goal in a record 31st straight game. Tom Dempsey of the New Orleans Saints kicks a 63-yard field goal, the longest in NFL history.

1971 COLLEGE—Cornell's Ed Marinaro finishes his career with a record 174.6 rushing yards per game. Oklahoma averages 472.4 rushing yards per game, smashing the old record by nearly 100 yards.

PRO—NFL attendance tops the 10 million mark for the first time.

1972 COLLEGE—Freshman are allowed to play varsity football.

PRO—The Miami Dolphins win a record 14 consecutive regular-season games on their way to a perfect season.

1973 COLLEGE—Mouth protectors become mandatory.

PRO—A jersey numbering system is adopted by the NFL, with 1–19 going to quarterbacks and "specialists," 20–49 to running backs and defensive backs, 50–59 for centers and linebackers, 60–79 for defensive linemen and offensive tackle and guards, and 80–89 for receivers. O. J. Simpson rushes for more than 2,000 yards to break Jim Brown's record.

1974 PRO—The NFL begins playing regular-season overtime games, adding an extra period to tie games, and several rules are changed to increase offense. The World Football League begins play, with several NFL stars on its rosters. The Toronto Northmen sign Miami superstars Larry Csonka, Jim Kiick, and Paul Warfield.

1975 COLLEGE—Ohio State halfback Archie Griffin becomes the first two-time Heisman Trophy winner.

PRO—George Blanda of the Oakland Raiders plays in his 26th and final season. The World Football League folds in October. Len Dawson of the Kansas City Chiefs leads the league in passing

percentage for a record eighth time.

1976 COLLEGE—Tony Dorsett of Pittsburgh finishes his career with a record 6,082 rushing yards.

PRO—The Tampa Bay Buccaneers and Seattle Seahawks join the NFL. The St. Louis Cardinals play the San Diego Chargers in Tokyo, Japan, prior to the season in the first pro football game held outside of North America.

1977 PRO—The Tampa Bay Buccaneers lose their 26th game in a row. Walter Payton gains a record 277 yards in a game against the Minnesota Vikings.

1978 The NFL expands its schedule from 14 to 16 games.

1979 COLLEGE—Top-ranked Alabama beats second-ranked Penn State in the Sugar Bowl to win the national championship.

PRO—The Los Angeles Rams win their division a record seventh time in a row.

1980 PRO—Bert Jones of the Baltimore Colts is sacked 12 times in a game. The post-season Pro Bowl game is moved to Hawaii. The Los Angeles Rams begin playing their games an hour south, in Anaheim. The NFL declines a request by the Oakland Raiders to move to Los Angeles, and Raider owner Al Davis sues the NFL.

1982 COLLEGE—Tear-away jerseys are eliminated by charging teams with a timeout when player need to change into new one. Northwestern beats Northern Illinois, ending a record 34-game losing streak. Herschel Walker of Georgia sets the all-time record for rushing yards in a three-year college career, with 5,259. Nebraska center Dave Rimington becomes the first two-time Outland Trophy winner.

PRO—A jury rules against the NFL and allows Al Davis to move the Raiders to Los Angeles. The season is interrupted by a 57-day player strike. Ken Anderson of the Cincinnati Bengals completes a record 70.6 percent of his passes. Dan Fouts of the San Diego Chargers leads the NFL in passing yards a record four years in a row.

1983 PRO—The Washington Redskins score a record 541 points in 16 games.

1984 COLLEGE—Doug Flutie of Boston College becomes the first college quarterback to amass 10,000 career passing yards.

PRO—The United States Football League, playing its games in the spring and summer, begins operation. The Colts abandon the city of Baltimore without warning and move in the middle of the night to Indianapolis, where they can play in a new domed stadium. Eric Dickerson of the Los Angeles Rams breaks O. J. Simpson's record with 2,105 yards, but does so in a 16-game season. Dan

Marino of the Miami Dolphins breaks NFL records with 48 touchdown passes and 5,084 yards. Mark Gastineau of the New York Jets gets 22 quarterback sacks—a record since sacks became an official stat.

1985 PRO—Lionel James of the San Diego Chargers gains a record 2,535 combined rushing, receiving, and return yards. In a span of a few hours, president Ronald Reagan is sworn in and flips a coin to determine who kicks off at Super Bowl XIX.

1986 COLLEGE—Running back Bo Jackson of Auburn is selected MVP of a bowl game for a record third straight season.

PRO—For the first time, instant replay is used to review official calls during games. Marcus Allen of the Los Angeles Raiders gains 100 yards in a record 11 straight games. Walter Payton of the Chicago Bears gains 1,000 yards in a season for the 10th time. Super Bowl XX edges the final episode of *M*A*S*H* as the most-watched television program in history, with 127 million viewers. A tape of the game is sent to Chinese television, where it is viewed by 300 million more people. The USFL loses its $1.7 billion lawsuit against the NFL and folds.

1987 PRO—The NFL begins broadcasting on ESPN. A player strike shortens the NFL schedule by one game. Joe Montana of the San

Francisco 49ers completes a record 22 consecutive passes over two games.

1988 COLLEGE—Barry Sanders of Oklahoma State gains a record 2,628 rushing yards, including an unprecedented five straight 200-yard games and 37 rushing touchdowns. His brother, Byron, eclipses the 1,000-yard mark for Northwestern the same year.

PRO—The St. Louis Cardinals move to Phoenix, Arizona.

1989 PRO—"Plan-B" free agency goes into effect, and more than 200 players switch teams. Flipper Anderson of the Los Angeles Rams amasses a record 336 receiving yards in a game. Art Shell of the Los Angeles Raiders becomes the league's first African-American head coach in nearly 70 years. Pete Rozelle retires and Paul Tagliabue is named the NFL's new commissioner.

1990 COLLEGE—Howard Griffith of Illinois scores a record eight rushing touchdowns in a game. David Klingler of Houston completes 374 passes for 5,140 yards, including 716 in a single game.

PRO—Fearing a lawsuit, the NFL changes its position on the draft, allowing teams to select college juniors if they have renounced their collegiate eligibility. The league adds two additional wild card teams to the playoffs. TNT

becomes the NFL's fourth broadcast partner, televising games on Sunday evenings. The league plays four preseason games outside the U.S., in Montreal, Tokyo, London, and Berlin. The San Francisco 49ers set a record with their 18th consecutive victory on the road.

1991 COLLEGE—The distance between uprights is narrowed by nearly five feet, to 18'6". Running back Tony Sands of Kansas gains 396 yards against Missouri. Quarterback Ty Detmer of Brigham Young finishes his college career with a record 15,031 passing yards and 151 touchdown passes.

PRO—The NFL establishes the World League of American Football to broaden football's appeal overseas. Warren Moon of the Houston Oilers completes a record 404 passes.

1992 PRO—The owners vote to abandon the use of instant replay to aid officials, feeling it makes games too long.

1993 COLLEGE—Bobby Dodd becomes only the second person enshrined in the College Football Hall of Fame as a player and a coach. Amos Alonzo Stagg was the first.

PRO—Miami Dolphin coach Don Shula picks up his 325th victory to surpass George Halas as the winningest coach in pro football history. Receiver Sterling Sharpe of the Green Bay Packers records the first back-to-back 100-catch seasons.

1994 COLLEGE—Miami loses to Washington, ending a record 58-game home winning streak that dates back to 1985. A record 63.5 million fans attend NCAA football games.

PRO—The passing game is greatly enhanced by new rules, including limiting contact between defensive backs and receivers. Two-point conversions are allowed for the first time since the 1960s. A preseason game in Mexico City draws 112,376 fans—the biggest crowd in pro football history. Steve Young of the San Francisco 49ers achieves a quarterback rating of 112.8, the highest ever.

1995 COLLEGE—Coach Eddie Robinson of Grambling wins his 400th game. Danny Wuerffel of Florida compiles a quarterback rating of 178.4, the highest in football history.

PRO—The Carolina Panthers and Jacksonville Jaguars begin play. The NFL becomes the first major sports league to establish a website on the internet. The Raiders move back to Oakland and the Rams move to St. Louis, leaving Los Angeles without a pro football team for the first time since 1945. Art Monk of the Philadelphia Eagles catches a pass in a record 183rd straight game. Emmitt Smith of the Dallas Cowboys scores a

record 25 touchdowns. Herman Moore of the Detroit Lions catches a record 123 passes. Carl Pickens of the Cincinnati Bengals ties an NFL record with 17 TD catches. Dan Marino becomes the NFL's all-time leader in completions, yards, and touchdowns. NFL attendance tops the 15 million mark for the first time.

1996 COLLEGE—The NCAA institutes an "overtime" tie-breaking system. 106,608 fans pay their way in to see Florida defeat Tennessee in Knoxville, the largest official regular-season crowd in NCAA history. Troy Davis of Iowa State becomes the first back-to-back 2,000-yard rusher in football history.

PRO—The Browns leave Cleveland after 50 seasons, becoming the Baltimore Ravens. John Kasay of the Carolina Panthers boots a record 37 field goals. Barry Sanders of the Detroit Lions becomes the first player to rush for more than 1,500 yards three times in his career. Jerry Rice catches 100 passes for a record third consecutive season, and becomes the first with 1,000 career receptions. Brett Favre becomes the league's second back-to-back MVP.

1997 COLLEGE—Nebraska completes its 36th consecutive winning season, the third-longest streak in history; Michigan's Charles Woodson becomes the first full-time defensive player to win the Heisman Trophy.

Pro—The Houston Oilers move to Nashville, Tennessee; Barry Sanders becomes the third player in history to rush for more than 2,000 yards in a season.

1998 **College**—Michigan and Nebraska, each undefeated, share the national championship.

Pro—John Elway guides the Denver Broncos past the Green Bay Packers in the Super Bowl, ending an eight-year winning streak by NFC teams.

APPENDIX A

AP National Collegiate Champions

1936	Minnesota
1937	Pittsburgh
1938	Texas Christian
1939	Texas A&M
1940	Minnesota
1941	Minnesota
1942	Ohio State
1943	Notre Dame
1944	Army
1945	Army
1946	Notre Dame
1947	Notre Dame
1948	Michigan
1949	Notre Dame
1950	Oklahoma
1951	Tennessee
1952	Michigan State
1953	Maryland
1954	Ohio State
1955	Oklahoma
1956	Oklahoma
1957	Auburn
1958	LSU
1959	Syracuse
1960	Minnesota
1961	Alabama
1962	Southern California
1963	Texas
1964	Alabama
1965	Alabama
1966	Notre Dame
1967	Southern California
1968	Ohio State
1969	Texas
1970	Nebraska
1971	Nebraska
1972	Southern California
1973	Notre Dame
1974	Oklahoma
1975	Oklahoma
1976	Pittsburgh
1977	Notre Dame
1978	Alabama
1979	Alabama
1980	Georgia
1981	Clemson
1982	Penn State
1983	Miami
1984	Brigham Young
1985	Oklahoma
1986	Penn State
1987	Miami
1988	Notre Dame
1989	Miami
1990	Colorado
1991	Miami
1992	Alabama
1993	Florida State
1994	Nebraska
1995	Nebraska
1996	Florida
1997	Michigan and Nebraska

APPENDIX B

Heisman Trophy Winners

1935	Jay Berwanger	RB	Chicago
1936	Larry Kelley	E	Yale
1937	Clint Frank	RB	Yale
1938	Davey O'Brien	QB	Texas Christian
1939	Nile Kinnick	RB	Iowa
1940	Tom Harmon	RB	Michigan
1941	Bruce Smith	RB	Minnesota
1942	Frank Sinkwich	RB	Georgia
1943	Angelo Betelli	QB	Notre Dame
1944	Les Horvath	QB	Ohio State
1945	Doc Blanchard	RB	Army
1946	Glenn Davis	RB	Army
1947	Johnny Lujack	QB	Notre Dame
1948	Doak Walker	RB	Southern Methodist
1949	Leon Hart	E	Notre Dame
1950	Vic Janowicz	RB	Ohio State
1951	Dick Kazmaier	RB	Princeton
1952	Billy Vessels	RB	Oklahoma

1953	Johnny Lattner	RB	Notre Dame
1954	Alan Ameche	RB	Wisconsin
1955	Howard Cassady	RB	Ohio State
1956	Paul Hornung	QB	Notre Dame
1957	John David Crow	RB	Texas A & M
1958	Pete Dawkins	RB	Army
1959	Billy Cannon	RB	LSU
1960	Joe Bellino	RB	Navy
1961	Ernie Davis	RB	Syracuse
1962	Terry Baker	QB	Oregon State
1963	Roger Staubach	QB	Navy
1964	John Huarte	QB	Notre Dame
1965	Mike Garrett	RB	Southern California
1966	Steve Spurrier	QB	Florida
1967	Gary Beban	QB	UCLA
1968	O. J. Simpson	RB	Southern California
1969	Steve Owens	RB	Oklahoma
1970	Jim Plunkett	QB	Stanford
1971	Pat Sullivan	QB	Auburn
1972	Johnny Rodgers	E	Nebraska
1973	John Cappelletti	RB	Penn State
1974	Archie Griffin	RB	Ohio State
1975	Archie Griffin	RB	Ohio State
1976	Tony Dorsett	RB	Pittsburgh
1977	Earl Campbell	RB	Texas
1978	Billy Sims	RB	Oklahoma
1979	Charles White	RB	Southern California
1980	George Rogers	RB	South Carolina
1981	Marcus Allen	RB	Southern California
1982	Herschel Walker	RB	Georgia
1983	Mike Rozier	RB	Nebraska
1984	Doug Flutie	QB	Boston College
1985	Bo Jackson	RB	Auburn
1986	Vinny Testaverde	QB	Miami
1987	Tim Brown	E	Notre Dame
1988	Barry Sanders	RB	Oklahoma State
1989	Andre Ware	QB	Houston
1990	Ty Detmer	QB	Brigham Young
1991	Desmond Howard	E	Michigan
1992	Gino Torretta	QB	Miami
1993	Charlie Ward	QB	Florida State
1994	Rashaan Salaam	RB	Colorado
1995	Eddie George	RB	Ohio State
1996	Danny Wuerffel	QB	Florida
1997	Charles Woodson	QB	Michigan

APPENDIX C
College Statistical Records

(All statistics through 1996 season)

Rushing Yards Per Game—Season

Player	School	Year	Yards/ Game
Barry Sanders	Oklahoma State	1988	238.9
Marcus Allen	Southern California	1981	212.9
Ed Marinaro	Cornell	1971	209.0
Troy Davis	Iowa State	1996	198.6
Byron Hanspard	Texas Tech	1996	189.5
Rashaan Salaam	Colorado	1994	186.8
Troy Davis	Iowa State	1995	182.7
Charles White	Southern California	1979	180.3
LeShon Johnson	Northern Illinois	1993	179.6
Mike Rozier	Nebraska	1983	179.0

Rushing Yards Per Game—Career

Player	School	Final Year	Yards/ Game
Ed Marinaro	Cornell	1971	174.6
O. J. Simpson	Southern California	1968	164.4
Herschel Walker	Georgia	1982	159.4
LeShon Johnson	Northern Illinois	1993	150.6
Marshall Faulk	San Diego State	1993	148.0
George Jones	San Diego State	1996	147.9
Tony Dorsett	Pittsburgh	1976	141.4
Troy Davis	Iowa State	1996	141.4
Mike Rozier	Nebraska	1983	136.6
Howard Stevens	Louisville	1972	136.2

Rushing Touchdowns—Career

Player	School	Final Year	Total TDs
Anthony Thompson	Indiana	1989	64
Marshall Faulk	San Diego State	1993	57
Steve Owens	Oklahoma	1969	56

Tony Dorsett	Pittsburgh	1976	55
Pete Johnson	Ohio State	1976	51
Mike Rozier	Nebraska	1983	50
Billy Sims	Oklahoma	1979	50
Ed Marinaro	Cornell	1971	50
Allen Pinkett	Notre Dame	1985	49
Herschel Walker	Georgia	1982	49
Ted Brown	North Carolina State	1978	49

Jim McMahon	Brigham Young	1980	176.9
Ty Detmer	Brigham Young	1989	175.6
Steve Sarkisian	Brigham Young	1996	173.6
Trent Dilfer	Fresno State	1993	173.1
Kerry Collins	Penn State	1994	172.9
Jerry Rhome	Tulsa	1964	172.6
Danny Wuerffel	Florida	1996	170.6
Bobby Hoying	Ohio State	1995	170.6
Billy Blanton	San Diego State	1996	169.6

Passing Yards Per Game—Season

Player	School	Year	Yards/Game
David Klingler	Houston	1990	467.3
Ty Detmer	Brigham Young	1990	432.3
Andre Ware	Houston	1989	427.2
Mike Maxwell	Nevada	1995	401.2
Scott Mitchell	Utah	1988	392.9
Chris Vargas	Nevada	1993	387.7
Jim McMahon	Brigham Young	1980	380.9
Ty Detmer	Brigham Young	1989	380.0
Troy Kopp	Pacific	1980	367.9
Jim McMahon	Brigham Young	1981	355.5

Passing Efficiency—Career

Player	School	Final Year	Rating
Danny Wuerffel	Florida	1996	163.6
Ty Detmer	Brigham Young	1991	162.7
Steve Sarkisian	Brigham Young	1996	162.0
Billy Blanton	San Diego State	1996	157.1
Jim McMahon	Brigham Young	1981	156.9
Steve Young	Brigham Young	1983	149.8
Robbie Bosco	Brigham Young	1985	149.4
Mike Maxwell	Nevada	1995	148.5
Chuck Long	Iowa	1985	147.8
John Walsh	Brigham Young	1994	147.8

Passing Yards Per Game—Career

Player	School	Final Year	Yards/Game
Ty Detmer	Brigham Young	1991	326.8
Chris Vargas	Nevada	1993	318.0
Mike Perez	San Jose State	1987	309.7
Doug Gaynor	Long Beach State	1985	308.8
Tony Eason	Illinois	1982	300.4
Steve Sarkisian	Brigham Young	1996	298.6
David Klingler	Houston	1991	295.8
Josh Wallwork	Wyoming	1996	293.3
Brent Snider	Utah State	1988	277.5
Mike Maxwell	Nevada	1995	268.7

Touchdown Passes—Season

Player	School	Year	Total TDs
David Klingler	Houston	1990	54
Jim McMahon	Brigham Young	1980	47
Andre Ware	Houston	1989	46
Ty Detmer	Brigham Young	1990	41
Danny Wuerffel	Florida	1996	39
Dennis Shaw	San Diego State	1969	39
Doug Williams	Grambling	1977	38
Troy Kopp	Pacific	1991	37
Danny Wuerffel	Florida	1995	35
Ty Detmer	Brigham Young	1991	35

Passing Efficiency—Season

Player	School	Year	Rating
Danny Wuerffel	Florida	1995	178.4

Touchdown Passes—Career

Player	School	Final Year	Total TDs
Ty Detmer	Brigham Young	1991	121

Danny Wuerffel	Florida	1996	114
David Klingler	Houston	1991	91
Troy Kopp	Pacific	1992	87
Jim McMahon	Brigham Young	1981	84
Joe Adams	Tennessee State	1980	81
John Elway	Stanford	1982	77
Andre Ware	Houston	1989	75
Shane Matthews	Florida	1992	74
Dan Marino	Pittsburgh	1982	74

Receptions—Season

Player	School	Year	Total Receptions
Manny Hazzard	Houston	1989	142
Howard Twilley	Tulsa	1965	134
Alex Van Dyke	Nevada	1995	129
Damon Wilkins	Nevada	1996	114
Marcus Harris	Wyoming	1996	109
Jason Phillips	Houston	1988	108
Fred Gilbert	Houston	1991	106
Chris Penn	Tulsa	1993	105
Sherman Smith	Houston	1992	103
James Dixon	Houston	1988	102

Receptions—Career

Player	School	Final Year	Total Receptions
Aaron Turner	Pacific	1992	266
Chad Mackey	Louisiana Tech	1996	264
Terance Mathis	New Mexico State	1989	263
Mark Templeton	Long Beach State	1986	262
Howard Twilley	Tulsa	1965	261
Marcus Harris	Wyoming	1996	259
David Williams	Illinois	1985	245
Marc Zeno	Tulane	1987	236
Jason Wolf	Southern Methodist	1992	235
Ryan Yarbrough	Wyoming	1993	229

Touchdown Catches—Season

Player	School	Year	Total TDs
Manny Hazzard	Houston	1989	22
Desmond Howard	Michigan	1991	19
Reidel Anthony	Florida	1996	18
Aaron Turner	Pacific	1991	18
Dennis Smith	Utah	1989	18
Tom Reynolds	San Diego State	1971	18
Terry Glenn	Ohio State	1995	17
Chris Doering	Florida	1995	17
Bryan Reeves	Nevada	1993	17
J. J. Stokes	UCLA	1993	17
Mario Bailey	Washington	1991	17
Clarkston Hines	Duke	1989	17

Touchdown Catches—Career

Player	School	Final Year	Total TDs
Aaron Turner	Pacific	1992	43
Ryan Yarbrough	Wyoming	1993	42
Marcus Harris	Wyoming	1996	38
Clarkston Hines	Duke	1989	38
Terance Mathis	New Mexico	1989	36
Elmo Wright	Houston	1970	34
Steve Largent	Tulsa	1975	32
Howard Twilley	Tulsa	1965	32
Chris Doering	Florida	1995	31
Lucious Davis	New Mexico State	1995	31
Bobby Engram	Penn State	1995	31
Manny Hazzard	Houston	1990	31

APPENDIX D
National Football League Champions

American Professional Football Association

(Champion named at end of season)

1920	Akron Pros
1921	Chicago Staleys

National Football League

(Champion named at end of season)

1922	Canton Bulldogs
1923	Canton Bulldogs
1924	Cleveland Bulldogs
1925	Chicago Cardinals
1926	Frankford Yellow Jackets
1927	New York Giants
1928	Providence Steam Roller
1929	Green Bay Packers
1930	Green Bay Packers
1931	Green Bay Packers
1932	Chicago Bears

Winner of NFL Championship Game

1933	Chicago Bears
1934	New York Giants
1935	Detroit Lions
1936	Green Bay Packers
1937	Washington Redskins
1938	New York Giants
1939	Green Bay Packers
1940	Chicago Bears
1941	Chicago Bears
1942	Washington Redskins
1943	Chicago Bears
1944	Green Bay Packers
1945	Cleveland Rams
1946	Chicago Bears
1947	Chicago Cardinals
1948	Philadelphia Eagles
1949	Philadelphia Eagles
1950	Cleveland Browns
1951	Los Angeles Rams
1952	Detroit Lions
1953	Detroit Lions
1954	Cleveland Browns
1955	Cleveland Browns
1956	New York Giants
1957	Detroit Lions
1958	Baltimore Colts
1959	Baltimore Colts
1960	Philadelphia Eagles
1961	Green Bay Packers
1962	Green Bay Packers
1963	Chicago Bears
1964	Cleveland Browns
1965	Green Bay Packers

Super Bowl Winners

Super Bowl No.	Year	NFL entry	AFL entry	Result	
I	1966	Green Bay Packers	Kansas City Chiefs	Green Bay	35-10
II	1967	Green Bay Packers	Oakland Raiders	Green Bay	33-14
III	1968	Baltimore Colts	New York Jets	New York	16-7
IV	1969	Minnesota Vikings	Kansas City Chiefs	Kansas City	23-7

Super Bowl No.	Year	National Football Conference	American Football Conference	Result	
V	1970	Dallas Cowboys	Baltimore Colts	Baltimore	16-13
VI	1971	Dallas Cowboys	Miami Dolphins	Dallas	24-3
VII	1972	Washington Redskins	Miami Dolphins	Miami	14-7
VIII	1973	Minnesota Vikings	Miami Dolphins	Miami	24-7
IX	1974	Minnesota Vikings	Pittsburgh Steelers	Pittsburgh	16-6

X	1975	Dallas Cowboys	Pittsburgh Steelers	Pittsburgh	21-17
XI	1976	Minnesota Vikings	Oakland Raiders	Oakland	32-14
XII	1977	Dallas Cowboys	Denver Broncos	Dallas	27-10
XIII	1978	Dallas Cowboys	Pittsburgh Steelers	Pittsburgh	35-31
XIV	1979	Los Angeles Rams	Pittsburgh Steelers	Pittsburgh	31-19
XV	1980	Philadelphia Eagles	Oakland Raiders	Oakland	27-10
XVI	1981	San Francisco 49ers	Cincinnati Bengals	San Francisco	26-21
XVII	1982	Washington	Miami Dolphins	Washington Redksins	27-17
XVIII	1983	Washington Redksins	Los Angeles Raiders	Los Angeles	38-9
XIX	1984	San Francisco 49ers	Miami Dolphins	San Francisco	38-16
XX	1985	Chicago Bears	New England Patriots	Chicago	46-10
XXI	1986	New York Giants	Denver Broncos	New York	39-20
XXII	1987	Washington Redskins	Denver Broncos	Washington	42-10
XXIII	1988	San Francisco 49ers	Cincinnati Bengals	San Francisco	20-16
XXIV	1989	San Francsico 49ers	Denver Broncos	San Francisco	55-10
XXV	1990	New York Giants	Buffalo Bills	New York	20-19
XXVI	1991	Washington Redskins	Buffalo Bills	Washington	37-24
XXVII	1992	Dallas Cowboys	Buffalo Bills	Dallas	52-17
XXVIII	1993	Dallas Cowboys	Buffalo Bills	Dallas	30-13
XXIX	1994	San Francisco 49ers	San Diego Chargers	San Francisco	49-26
XXX	1995	Dallas Cowboys	Pittsburgh Steelers	Dallas	27-17
XXXI	1996	Green Bay Packers	New England Patriots	Green Bay	35-21
XXXII	1997	Green Bay Packers	Denver Broncos	Denver	31-24

APPENDIX E
Champions of Rival Professional Football Leagues

American Football League I (1926)
1926 Philadelphia Quakers

American Football League II (1936–37)
1936 Boston Shamrocks
1937 Los Angeles Bulldogs

American Football League III (1940–41)
1940 Columbus Bullies
1941 Columbus Bullies

All-American Football Conference (1946–49)
1946 Cleveland Browns
1947 Cleveland Browns
1948 Cleveland Browns
1949 Cleveland Browns

American Football League IV (1960–69)
1960 Houston Oilers
1961 Houston Oilers
1962 Dallas Texans
1963 San Diego Chargers
1964 Buffalo Bills
1965 Buffalo Bills
1966 Kansas City Chiefs
1967 Oakland Raiders
1968 New York Jets
1969 Kansas City Chiefs

1987	John Elway	QB	Denver Broncos
1988	Boomer Esiason	QB	Cincinnati Bengals
1989	Joe Montana	QB	San Francisco 49ers
1990	Joe Montana	QB	San Francisco 49ers
1991	Thurman Thomas	RB	Buffalo Bills
1992	Steve Young	QB	San Francisco 49ers
1993	Emmitt Smith	RB	Dallas Cowboys
1994	Steve Young	QB	San Francisco 49ers
1995	Brett Favre	QB	Green Bay Packers
1996	Brett Favre	QB	Green Bay Packers

World Football League (1974)

1974	Birmingham Americans

United States Football League (1983–85)

1983	Michigan Panthers
1984	Philadelphia Stars
1985	Baltimore Stars

APPENDIX F
NFL Most Valuable Player Awards

1957	Jim Brown	RB	Cleveland Browns
1958	Gino Marchetti	DE	Baltimore Colts
1959	Charley Conerley	QB	New York Giants
1960 (tie)	Norm Van Brocklin	QB	Philadelphia Eagles
	Joe Schmidt	LB	Detroit Lions
1961	Paul Hornung	RB	Green Bay Packers
1962	Jim Taylor	RB	Green Bay Packers
1963	Y. A. Tittle	QB	New York Giants
1964	Johnny Unitas	QB	Baltimore Colts
1965	Jim Brown	RB	Cleveland Browns
1966	Bart Starr	QB	Green Bay Packers
1967	Johnny Unitas	QB	Baltimore Colts
1968	Earl Morrall	QB	Baltimore Colts
1969	Roman Gabriel	QB	Los Angeles Rams
1970	John Brodie	QB	San Francisco 49ers
1971	Alan Page	DT	Minnesota Vikings
1972	Larry Brown	RB	Washington Redskins
1973	O. J. Simpson	RB	Buffalo Bills
1974	Ken Stabler	QB	Oakland Raiders
1975	Fran Tarkenton	QB	Minnesota Vikings
1976	Bert Jones	QB	Baltimore Colts
1977	Walter Payton	RB	Chicago Bears
1978	Terry Bradshaw	QB	Pittsburgh Steelers
1979	Earl Campbell	RB	Houston Oilers
1980	Brian Sipe	QB	Cleveland Browns
1981	Ken Anderson	QB	Cincinnati Bengals
1982	Mark Moseley	K	Washington Redskins
1983	Joe Theismann	QB	Washington Redskins
1984	Dan Marino	QB	Miami Dolphins
1985	Marcus Allen	RB	Los Angeles Raiders
1986	Lawrence Taylor	LB	New York Giants

APPENDIX G
Professional Football Statistical Records

(All statistics through 1996 regular season)

Rushing Yards—Season

Player	Team	Year	Total Yards
Eric Dickerson	Los Angeles Rams	1984	2,105
O. J. Simpson	Buffalo Bills	1973	2,003
Earl Campbell	Houston Oilers	1980	1,934
Barry Sanders	Detroit Lions	1994	1,883
Jim Brown	Cleveland Browns	1963	1,863
Walter Payton	Chicago Bears	1977	1,852
Eric Dickerson	Los Angeles Rams	1986	1,821
O. J. Simpson	Buffalo Bills	1975	1,817
Eric Dickerson	Los Angeles Rams	1983	1,808
Emmitt Smith	Dallas Cowboys	1995	1,773

Rushing Yards—Career

Player	Total Yards
Walter Payton	16,726
Eric Dickerson	13,259
Tony Dorsett	12,739
Jim Brown	12,312
Franco Harris	12,120
Marcus Allen	11,738
Barry Sanders	11,725
John Riggins	11,352

O. J. Simpson	11,236
Thurman Thomas	10,762
Emmitt Smith	10,160

Yards Per Carry—Season

Player	Team	Year	Yards/Carry
Beattie Feathers	Chicago Bears	1934	9.9
Randall Cunningham	Philadelphia Eagles	1990	7.8
Bobby Douglass	Chicago Bears	1972	6.9
Joe Perry	San Francisco 49ers	1949	6.8
Dan Towler	Los Angeles Rams	1951	6.5
Johnny Strzykalski	San Francisco 49ers	1948	6.5
Keith Lincoln	San Diego Chargers	1963	6.5
Mercury Morris	Miami Dolphins	1973	6.4
Jim Brown	Cleveland Browns	1963	6.4
Johnny Strzykalski	San Francisco 49ers	1947	6.3

Yards Per Carry—Career

Player	Yards/Carry
Marion Motley	5.7
Jim Brown	5.2
Mercury Morris	5.1
Joe Perry	5.0
Gale Sayers	5.0
Barry Sanders	4.9
Paul Lowe	4.9
Lenny Moore	4.8
Tony Nathan	4.8
Marv Hubbard	4.8

Passing Yards—Season

Player	Team	Year	Total Yards
Dan Marino	Miami Dolphins	1984	5,084
Dan Fouts	San Diego Chargers	1981	4,802
Dan Marino	Miami Dolphins	1986	4,746
Dan Fouts	San Diego Chargers	1980	4,715
Warren Moon	Houston Oilers	1991	4,690
Warren Moon	Houston Oilers	1990	4,689
Neil Lomax	St. Louis Cardinals	1984	4,619
Drew Bledsoe	New England Patriots	1994	4,555
Lynn Dickey	Green Bay Packers	1983	4,458
Dan Marino	Miami Dolphins	1994	4,453

Passing Yards—Career

Player	Total Yards
Dan Marino	51,636
Fran Tarkenton	47,003
John Elway	45,034
Warren Moon	43,787
Dan Fouts	43,040
Joe Montana	40,551
Johnny Unitas	40,239
Dave Krieg	37,946
Boomer Esiason	36,442
Jim Kelly	35,467

Touchdown Passes—Season

Player	Team	Year	Total TDs
Dan Marino	Miami Dolphins	1984	48
Dan Marino	Miami Dolphins	1986	44
Brett Favre	Green Bay Packers	1996	39
Brett Favre	Green Bay Packers	1995	38
George Blanda	Houston Oilers	1961	36
Y. A. Tittle	New York Giants	1963	36
Steve Young	San Francisco 49ers	1994	35
Daryle Lamonica	Oakland Raiders	1969	34
Y. A. Tittle	New York Giants	1962	33

Dan Fouts	San Diego Chargers	1981	33
Warren Moon	Houston Oilers	1990	33
Jim Kelly	Buffalo Bills	1991	33
Brett Favre	Green Bay Packers	1994	33
Warren Moon	Houston Oilers	1995	33
Vinny Testaverde	Baltimore Ravens	1996	33

Touchdown Passes—Career

Player	Total TDs
Dan Marino	369
Fran Tarkenton	342
Johnny Unitas	290
Joe Montana	273
Dave Krieg	261
Sonny Jurgensen	255
Dan Fouts	254
Warren Moon	254
John Elway	251
John Hadl	244

Receptions—Season

Player	Team	Year	Total Receptions
Herman Moore	Detroit Lions	1995	123
Jerry Rice	San Francisco 49ers	1995	122
Cris Carter	Minnesota Vikings	1995	122
Cris Carter	Minnesota Vikings	1994	122
Isaac Bruce	St. Louis Rams	1995	119
Jerry Rice	San Francisco 49ers	1994	112
Sterling Sharpe	Green Bay Packers	1993	112
Michael Irvin	Dallas Cowboys	1995	111
Terance Mathis	Atlanta Falcons	1994	111
Jerry Rice	San Francisco 49ers	1996	108
Brett Perriman	Detroit Lions	1995	108
Sterling Sharpe	Green Bay Packers	1992	108

Receptions—Career

Player	Total Receptions
Jerry Rice	1,050
Art Monk	940
Steve Largent	819
Henry Ellard	775
Andre Reed	766
James Lofton	764
Charlie Joiner	750
Gary Clark	699
Cris Carter	667
Ozzie Newsome	662

Touchdown Catches—Season

Player	Team	Year	Total TDs
Jerry Rice	San Francisco 49ers	1987	22
Mark Clayton	Miami Dolphins	1984	18
Sterling Sharpe	Green Bay Packers	1994	18
Don Hutson	Green Bay Packers	1942	17
Elroy Hirsch	Los Angeles Rams	1951	17
Bill Groman	Houston Oilers	1961	17
Jerry Rice	San Francisco 49ers	1989	17
Carl Pickens	Cincinnati Bengals	1995	17
Cris Carter	Minnesota Vikings	1995	17
Art Powell	New York Titans	1960	16
Cloyce Box	Detroit Lions	1952	15
Sonny Randle	St. Louis Cardinals	1960	15
Jerry Rice	San Francisco 49ers	1986	15
Jerry Rice	San Francisco 49ers	1993	15
Andre Rison	Atlanta Falcons	1993	15
Jerry Rice	San Francisco 49ers	1995	15

Touchdown Catches—Career

Player	Total TDs
Jerry Rice	154
Steve Largent	100
Don Hutson	99
Don Maynard	88
Lance Alworth	85

Paul Warfield   85
Tommy McDonald   84
Mark Clayton   84
Art Powell   81
Charley Taylor   79
Harold Carmichael   79

Points Scored—season

Player	Team	Year	Total Points
Paul Hornung	Green Bay Packers	1960	176
Mark Moseley	Washington Redskins	1983	161
Gino Cappelletti	Boston Patriots	1964	155
Emmitt Smith	Dallas Cowboys	1995	150
Chip Lohmiller	Washington Redskins	1991	149
Gino Cappelletti	Boston Patriots	1961	147
Paul Hornung	Green Bay Packers	1961	146

Jim Turner	New York Jets	1968	145
John Kasay	Carolina Panthers	1996	145
John Riggins	Washington Redskins	1983	144
Kevin Butler	Chicago Bears	1985	144

Points—Career

Player	Total Points
George Blanda	2,002
Nick Lowery	1,711
Jan Stenerud	1,699
Gary Anderson	1,556
Morten Andersen	1,537
Eddie Murray	1,473
Pat Leahy	1,470
Norm Johnson	1,452
Jim Turner	1,439
Matt Bahr	1,422

APPENDIX H

Members of the Pro Football Hall of Fame

Quarterbacks

Sammy Baugh
George Blanda
Terry Bradshaw
Dutch Clark
Len Dawson
Paddy Driscoll
Dan Fouts
Otto Graham
Bob Griese
Arnie Herber
Sonny Jurgenson
Bobby Layne
Sid Luckman
Joe Namath
Ace Parker
Bart Starr
Roger Staubach
Fran Tarkenton
Y. A. Tittle
Johnny Unitas
Norm Van Brocklin
Bob Waterfield

Running Backs

Cliff Battles
Jim Brown
Earl Campbell
Tony Canadeo
Larry Csonka
Tony Dorsett
Bill Dudley
Frank Gifford
Red Grange
Joe Guyon
Franco Harris
Clark Hinkle
Paul Hornung
Leroy Kelly
Tuffy Leemans
Ollie Matson
George McAfee
Hugh McElhenny
Johnny Blood McNally
Bobby Mitchell
Lenny Moore
Marion Motley
Bronko Nagurski
Ernie Nevers
Walter Payton
Joe Perry
John Riggins
Gale Sayers
O. J. Simpson
Ken Strong
Jim Taylor
Jim Thorpe
Charlie Trippi
Steve Van Buren
Doak Walker

Receivers/Ends

Lance Alworth
Red Badgro
Raymond Berry
Fred Biletnikoff
Guy Chamberlain
Mike Ditka

Tom Fears
Bill Hewitt
Elroy Hirsch
Don Hutson
Charlie Joiner
Steve Largent
Dante Lavelli
John Mackey
Don Maynard
Tommy McDonald
Wayne Millner
Pete Pihos
Jackie Smith
Charley Taylor
Paul Warfield
Kellen Winslow

Offensive Linemen

Chuck Bednarik
Roosevelt Brown
Lou Creekmur
Dan Dierdorf
Turk Edwards
Dan Fortmann
Frank Gatski
Forrest Gregg
John Hannah
Ed Healey
Mel Hein
Pete Henry
Cal Hubbard
Stan Jones
Walt Kiesling
Bruiser Kinard
Jim Langer
Larry Little
Link Lyman

Mike McCormack
Mike Michalske
Ron Mix
George Musso
Anthony Munoz
Jim Otto
Jim Parker
Jim Ringo
Bob St. Clair
Art Shell
Dwight Stephenson
Joe Stydahar
George Trafton
Bulldog Turner
Gene Upshaw
Mike Webster
Bill Willis
Alex Wojciechowicz

Defensive Linemen

Doug Atkins
Buck Buchanan
Willie Davis
Art Donovan
Len Ford
Joe Greene
Deacon Jones
Henry Jordan
Bob Lilly
Gino Marchetti
Leo Nomellini
Merlin Olsen
Alan Page
Andy Robustelli
Lee Roy Selmon
Ernie Stautner
Arnie Weinmeister

Randy White

Linebackers

Bobby Bell
Dick Butkus
George Connor
Bill George
Jack Ham
Ted Hendricks
Sam Huff
Jack Lambert
Willie Langer
Ray Nitschke
Joe Schmidt
Mike Singletary

Defensive Backs

Herb Adderley
Lem Barney
Mel Blount
Willie Brown
Jack Christiansen
Mike Haynes
Ken Houston
Jimmy Johnson
Paul Krausse
Night Train Lane
Yale Lary
Mel Renfro
Emlen Tunnell
Larry Wilson
Willie Wood

Specialists

Lou Groza
Jan Stenerud

Coaches

Paul Brown
Jimmy Conzelman
Weeb Ewbank
Ray Flaherty
Joe Gibbs
Sid Gillman
Bud Grant
George Halas
Curly Lambeau
Tom Landry
Vince Lombardi
Greasy Neale
Chuck Noll
Steve Owen
Don Shula
Bill Walsh

Owners & League Officials

Bert Bell
Charlie Bidwell
Joe Carr
Al Davis
Jim Finks
Lamar Hunt
Tim Mara
Wellington Mara
George Preston Marshall
Shorty Ray
Dan Reeves
Art Rooney
Pete Rozelle
Tex Schramm

For More Information

Books

Bliss, Jonathan. *Dynasties.* Vero Beach, FL: Rourke, 1992.

Brenner, Richard J. *The Complete Super Bowl Story.* Minneapolis: Lerner, 1990.

Campbell, Jim. *Golden Years of Pro Football.* New York: Crescent Books, 1993.

Carroll, Bob. *100 Greatest Running Backs.* New York: Crescent Books, 1989.

Gershman, Michael, Bob Carroll, and David Neft, eds. *Total Football: The Official Encyclopedia of the National Football League.* New York: HarperCollins, 1997.

Gutman, Bill. *Sports Illustrated's Pro Football Record Breakers.* New York: Pocket Books, 1990.

————. *Great Moments in Pro Football.* New York: Pocket Books, 1991.

————. *Great Quarterbacks of the NFL.* New York: Pocket Books, 1995.

Italia, Bob. *100 Unforgettable Moments in Pro Football.* Minneapolis: Abdo & Daughters, 1996

Rockwell, Bart. *World's Strangest Football Stories.* Mahway, NJ: Troll, 1992

For Advanced Readers

Ashe, Arthur R., Jr. *A Hard Road to Glory: A History of the African-American Athlete.* 2 vols. New York: Warner, 1988.

Halecroft, David. *Good Days, Bad Days; An NFL Book.* New York: Viking Press, 1992.

Peterson, Robert W. *Pigskin: The Early Years of Pro Football.* New York: Oxford University Press, 1997.

Whittingham, Richard. *What a Game They Played.* New York: Simon & Schuster, 1988.

Wimmer, Dick (ed.). *The Gridiron Game: An Anthology of Football Writings.* Masters Press, 1997.

Internet

http://collegefootball.org/
This is the home page of the College Football Hall of Fame; features biographies and statistics on the hall's more than 700 members.

http://www.evansville.net/wajl10/
This site is a clearinghouse of college football information: bowl results, Heisman Trophy winners, team schedules, national polls, and statistics on Division 1-A individual category leaders are all featured.

http://www.sportingnews.com/cfootball/
College football site of *The Sporting News.* Commentary, team reports, up-to-date news.

http://www.nfl.com
The official site of the National Football League. Detailed biographies of active players and links to official team sites.

http://www.dickbutkus.com/
The Dick Butkus Football Network site features information on every level of organized football, from the NFL to Pop Warner leagues. Includes regular columns by the inimitable Butkus and many of his contemporaries, including Deacon Jones.

http://www.nflhistory.com/
A massive trove of information on the history of the NFL, with biographies of Hall of Fame players, sidebars on the greatest playoff games, notable off-field events, and the league's beginnings.

http://nflfans.com/
A central clearinghouse for fans, this site offers up-to-the-minute news on every NFL team. It also includes links to the best fan-maintained team sites.

Index

Page numbers in *italics* indicate illustrations.

Adams, Bud, 62
Aikman, Troy, 107, 108, 112
Aldrich, Ki, 43
All-American Football Conference (AAFC), 53–55, 57
Allegheny Athletic Association, 20, 21
Allen, Marcus, 90, 91, 92
Alworth, Lance, 67
Amateur Athletic Union, 20, 21
Ameche, Alan "The Horse," 60, 61
American Football League (AFL), 62, 64–68, *65,* 74, 100
American Professional Football Association (APFA), 35–36, 41
Army. *See* Military Academy, U.S.
Arnold, William, 9

Baltimore Colts, 54, 59–61, 69, 75, 76, 81, 98
Baugh, Sammy, 43, 47, *47,* 49, 113
Bell, Bert, 66
Bell, Ricky, 77–78
Berry, Dave, 22
Berry, Raymond, *59,* 60, 61
Berwanger, Jay, 44
Bevan, Bill, 45
Bierman, Bernie, 45
Blaik, Earl "Red," 50
Blanchard, Doc, 50–51, *51*
Blanda, George, 65, 67
Blozis, Al, 50
Bollinger, Bo, 52
Bowden, Bobby, 101
Boydston, Max, 52
Bradshaw, Terry, 84, 88
Brallier, John, 21, 22
Brigham Young University, 88
Brodie, John, 69
Brooke, George, 21
Brown, Jim, 52–53, 71–72, *71,* 79, 86
Brown, Paul, 55–56, *56,* 58
Brown, Roger, 76, *76,* 77
Brown, Tim, 89, 112
Bryant, Paul "Bear," 61–62, *63,* 64, 75, 85
Buchanan, Buck, 64

Buffalo Bills, 67, 85, 108, 110–11
Burris, Kurt, 52
Butkus, Dick, 64, 72, *72*

Calac, Pete, 34
Camp, Walter, *9,* 10–11, 14, *15,* 18 24, 28
Campbell, Earl, 79, 91, 97
Canadian Football League (CFL), 59, 65, 67
Cannon, Billy, 65
Canton Bulldogs, 23–24, *23,* 33, 34, 35, 41
Carlisle Indian School, 27, 31–32, 38
Carr, Joe, 36
Carson, Harry, 98, 99
Carter, Cris, 89, 112
Chamberlain, Guy, 41
Chicago Athletic Club, 20–21
Chicago Bears, 36, 39–41, 43, 46, 48, 49, *49,* 54, 55, 65, 72–73, 86, 92–93
Chicago Cardinals, 40, 50, 59, 66
Cleveland Browns, 54–56, 58, 67, 71, 72, 81, 82
Cleveland Rams, 50, 53, 55
College football, 5–19, 24–33, 34, 36–39, 41–46, 49–53, 54, 61–64, 73–80, 86–91, 101–6
Connor, George, 51
Constable, Pepper, 44
Corbin, Pa, 14
Cotton Bowl, 42, 79
Coy, Ted, 31
Crawford, Fred, 43
Crisher, Bill, 52
Crowley, Jim, 37, *38*
Csonka, Larry, 81, 82, *82,* 87

Dallas Cowboys, 66, 80–81, *80,* 85, 107–8, 109, 110
Dalrymple, Jerry, 43
Davidson, Gary, 87
Davis, Al, 74, 100, *100*
Davis, Glenn, 50–51, *51, 57*
Davis, Willie, 71
Dawkins, Pete, 53
Decatur Staleys, 34–35, *34,* 36, 41
Deland, Lorin, 17
Denver Broncos, 95, 97, 113
Detroit Lions, 58, 66, 76, 111
Devine, Dan, 79
Dickerson, Eric, 90, 91, 97–98
Dinkey, A.C., 22
Ditka, Mike, 93

Donnelly, Ben "Sport," 21
Donovan, Art, 61
Dorias, Gus, 28–29
Dorsett, Tony, 78–79, *78,* 81
Downtown Athletic Club, 44
Dreyfuss, Barney, 22

Ellis, William Webb, 5
Elway, John, 89, 97, 112, 113
Erickson, Dennis, 88, 101

Faulk, Marshall, 103–4
Favre, Brett, 109–10, 112
Fears, Tom, 57, 58
Feathers, Beattie, 48, 59
Fiscus, Lawton, 21
Florida State University, 101, 102, 103
Flutie, Doug, 87, 89–90, *89*
Follis, Charles, 23
Franck, George, 45
Frazier, Tommy, 102, 103, 105, 106
Friedman, Benny, 42–43, *42*

Gambling, 20, 24, 33, 66
"Game, The," 60
Gastineau, Mark, 99, *99*
George, Bill, 72
Gibbs, Joe, 92
Gifford, Frank, *58,* 59, 60
Gilliam, Joe, 55
Gillom, Horace, 55, 56
Gipp, George, 31, 33
Graham, Otto, 56, 58
Grange, Red, 36, 37–38, 39–41, *40,* 42
Grant, Bud, 83
Granted, Henry, 8
Green Bay Packers, 36, 41, 47, 69–71, 74, 109–10, 113
Greene, "Mean" Joe, 83, *84*
Greenwood, L.C., 83, *84*
Grier, Rosey, 77
Griffin, Archie, 78
Groza, Lou "The Toe," 56, *57*
Guyon, Joe, 34

Hadl, John, 67
Halas, George, 34–35, 36, 40, 41, 46, 49, *49,* 54, 66
Harmon, Tom, 44
Harper, Jesse, 28–29

Harris, Franco, 84–85
Hart, Leon, 51
Harvard University, 5–6, 7–9, 10, 11, 13, 16, 17, 18, *19,* 20, 24, 26, 31
Hay, Ralph, 35
Heffelfinger, Pudge, 14, *15,* 20–21
Heisman Memorial Trophy, 44, 45, 46, 50, 51, 52, 53, 57, 62, 64, 65, 73, 78, 79, 89, 90, 103, 104, 105
Hennigan, Charley, 65–67
Hering, Frank, 27
Heston, Willie, 24
High school football, 6, 27–28
Hill, Calvin, 81, 87
Hirsch, Elroy, 57
Hoerner, Dick, 57
Holmgren, Mike, 109–10
Hornung, Paul, 66, 70, *70,* 71
Houston Oilers, 65, 67, 74, 97
Hudson, Dick, 76
Hunt, Lamar, 62, *74*
Hutson, Don, 43, 47–48, *48*

Intercollegiate Athletic Association (IAA), 24, 28
Intercollegiate Football Association, 9, 10, 13
Irvin, Michael, 107, 108

Johnson, Jimmy, 88, 107
Johnson, John Henry, 59
Jones, Deacon, *76,* 77
Jordan, Lee Roy, 64, 81
Jurgensen, Sonny, 68

Kansas City Chiefs, 67, 74, 82
Karras, Alex, 66, 76
Kavanagh, Ken, 49
Kelly, Jim, 88, 110
Kemp, Jack, 65, 68
Kiick, Jim, 81, 87
Kinard, Bruiser, 43
Kinnick, Nile, 45, *45*
King, Philip, 17, 18
King, Ray, 45
Kramer, Jerry, *70,* 71

Lambeau, Curly, 41
Lambert, Jack, 85
Lamonica, Daryl, 67–68, 87
Landry, Tom, 80–81, *80,* 107, 108

Lane, "Night Train," 55
Larson, Butch, 45
Lavelli, Dante, 56
Layden, Elmer, 37, *38*
Layne, Bobby, 58
Leahy, Frank, 51
Lipscomb, Big Daddy, 61
Lombardi, Vince, 59, 69–71, *69*
Los Angeles Rams, 53, 54–55, 56–58, 59, 66,
    76–77, 97, 100
Lott, Ronnie, 94–95
Luckman, Sid, 49
Lujack, Johnny, 51
Lund, Pug, 45
Lundy, Lamar, *76, 77*

McAfee, George, 49
McDonald, Tommy, 52
McElhenney, Hugh, 59
McGill University, 7–9
Mack, Connie, 22
McMahon, Jim, 88, 92–93
McNair, Steve, 104–5, 106
Madden, John, 85
Mahan, Eddie, 31
Mann, Bob, 55
Manning, Peyton, 104, *104,* 105
Mara, Tim, 42
Marino, Dan, 89, 95–97, *96* 112–13
Marshall, George Preston, 46, 66
Martin Harvey "Too Mean," 81
Maryland, Russell, 89, 107
Massillon Tigers, 23–24, *23,* 33, 34
Merriwell, Frank, 31
Meyer, Monk, 44
Miami Dolphins, 80, 81–83, 85, 95–97
Military Academy, U.S., 24, 28–29, 31, 33, 44,
    49–51, 53
Miller, Don, 37, *38*
Minnesota Vikings, 66, 68–69, 80, 82, 83, 85, 107,
    111
Montana, Joe, 79–80, 93–94, 95, *95,* 96–97, 108, 113
Moore, Lenny, 60, 61
Morris, Mercury, 81, 82
Morton, Craig, 80, 81
Motley, Marion, 54, 55, 56, *57,* 58

Nagurski, Bronko, 38–39, 48, *49,* 56

Namath, Joe, 62, 64, 68, *68,* 69, 74, 75, *75,* 87, 88,
    96
National Collegiate Athletic Association (NCAA),
    24, 73
National Football League (NFL), 22, 36, 39, 41,
    53–55, 56, 57, 58, 64, 65, 66, 67, 100, 101, 105,
    106
Nevers, Ernie, 38, 40
New York Giants, 40, 42–43, 50, 59, 69, 70, 74, 76,
    77, 82, 98–99
New York Jets, 68, 74, 81, 82, 99
Nitschke, Ray, 71
Nobis, Tommy, 64
Noll, Chuck, 83, 84
Notre Dame University, 13, 28–29, 33, 35, 36–37,
    38, 39, 44, 45, 51, 67, 77, 79, 89, 93

Oakland Raiders, 68, 74, 83, 84, 85, 92, 100
Odson, Urban, 45
Olsen, Merlin, *76, 77*
Oneida Football Club, 6
Orange Bowl, 42, 64, 101, 102–3, 104
Osborne, Tom, 101
Osmanski, Bill, 49

Page, Alan, 83
Parcells, Bill, 99
Paterno, Joe, 89
Payton, Walter, 86, 92, *93*
Pennsylvania State University, 13, 84, 89
Perry, Joe "The Jet," 59
Perry, William "The Refrigerator," 92
Philadelphia Eagles, 50, 59, 68, 70, 92, 99
Pierce, Palmer, 24
Pittsburgh Steelers, 50, 55, 59, 67, 80, 82, 83–85, 108
Players Association, 101, 106
Plunkett, Jim, 79, 92
Pollard, Fritz, 35, 54, 55
Prince, Billy, 22
Princeton University, 6–7, 9, 10, 11, 13, 14, 15, 17,
    18, 21, 24, 44
Professional football, 19–24, 33–36, 39–41, 42,
    46–49, 53–61, 62, 64–73, 74–75, 76–77, 80–86,
    87, 91–101, 106–13
  integration of, 35, 54–55
Pyle, C.C., 39, 40, 41

Rice, Grantland, 37

Rice, Jerry, 48, 95, *95,* 109, 112, 113, *113*
Roberts, J.D., 52
Robeson, Paul, 35, *35*
Robinson, Eddie, 26
Robinson, Jackie, 54
Rockne, Knute, 28–29, 33, 36–37, *37,* 39, 51
Roger, David, 8
Rogers, Art, 22
Rooney, Art, 83
Roosevelt, Theodore, 24
Rose Bowl, 38, 39, 78
Rote, Tobin, 67
Rozelle, Pete, 66, 74, *74,* 93, 100, 101
Rozier, Mike, 87, 90
Rugby, 5–9, *5,* 12, 53
Rules, 6–14, 18, 24–25, 28–29, 46, 107
Rutgers University, 6–7
Ryan, Buddy, 93

St. Louis University, 26–27
Sanders, Barry, 90–91, 111, 113
San Diego Chargers, 67, 76, 93, 109, 113
San Francisco 49ers, 53, 54, 55, 59, 69, 92, 93–95,
    96–97, 108–9
Sayers, Gale, 63, 72–73, *73,* 111
Schneider, Jack, 26
Schnellenberger, Howard, 88, 107
Seifert, George, 108
Shakespeare, Bill, 44
Shell, Art, 55
Shula, Don, 81–83, 96
Simpson, O.J., 62–62, 64, 77, 85–86, *86,* 97
Sims, Billy, 78
Singletary, Mike, 93
Sinnock, Pomeroy, 27
Sitko, Emil, 51
Slater, Duke, 54
Smith, Bruce, 45–46
Smith, Bruce, 110–11, *111*
Smith, Bubba, 64, *64*
Smith, Emmitt, 91, 103, 107, *107,* 108, 111
Smith, "Vitamin," 57
Speedie, Mac, 56, 58
Spurrier, Steve, 101
Stabler, Ken, 62, 85, 87
Stagg, Amos Alonzo, 14, 15–17, *15,* 18, 27, *27*
Staley, A.E., 34, 36
Stanford University, 38, 39, 69, 89, 108

Starr, Bart, 70, *70,* 71, 74
Staubach, Roger, 63–64, *63,* 80, 81, 88
Stewart, Kordell, 103, 105
Stram, Hank, 67
Strode, Woody, 54
Stuhlreder, Harry, 37, *38*
Suffridge, Bob, 43
Sugar Bowl, 42, 62, 101
Super Bowl, 74–75, 80, 81, 83, 85, 92, 93, 94,
    96–97, 99, 108, 109, 113
Switzer, Barry, 78, 108
Swann, Lynn, 85, *85*

Tagliabue, Paul, 106
Tarkenton, Fran, 68–69, 83
Taylor, Jim, 70–71, *70*
Taylor, Lawrence, 98–99
Television, 60, 66, 73, 87, 99, 106
Temple, William, 22
Thomas, Thurman, 90–91, 110, 111
Thorpe, Jim, 31–32, *32,* 33, 34, 35, 36, 40, 41
Tinsley, Gaynell, 43
Tittle, Y.A., 59, *67*
Towler, Dan, 57
Trafton, George, 35
Triplett, Wally, 55
Tripucka, Frank, 65
Tubbs, Jerry, 52
Tunnell, Emlen, 55
Turner, Bulldog, 49

Unitas, Johnny, 59–61, *60,* 69, 82, 95, 113
United States Football League (USFL), 87, 90
University of Alabama, 61–62, 64, 68, 75–77, 85, 101
University of Chicago, 16, 27, 44
University of Florida, 91, 101, 107
University of Illinois, 27, 34, 35, 37, 39, 64
University of Miami, 83, 88–89, 101, 102–3, 107
University of Michigan, 13, 24, 38, 39, 42, 44, 45,
    88, 90, 103
University of Minnesota, 13, 38, 45–46
University of Nebraska, 90, 101–3
University of Oklahoma, 29, 51–52, 78
University of Pennsylvania, 13, 14, 17, 18, 21, 31,
    32, 38
University of Pittsburgh, 31, 78–79, 96
University of Southern California, 13, 59, 62,
    77–78, 90, 94

Van Brocklin, Norm, 56–57, 58
Van Buren, Steve, 58–59
Vessels, Billy, 52

Walker, Herschel, 87, 90, *90,* 91, 103, 107
Wallace, Blondy, 24
Walsh, Bill, 93–95, *94,* 108
Ward, Charlie, 101, *103,* 105
Warfield, Paul, 81, 87
Warner, Pop, 22, 27, 32, 38
Washington, Kenny, 54–55
Washington Redskins, 46, 49, 55, 68, 82, 92
Waterfield, Bob, 56
Weatherall, Jim, 52
White, Byron "Whizzer," 43–44
White, Charles, 77–78, 90

White, Reggie, 99, 110, *110*
Widseth, Ed, 45
Wilkinson, Bud, 51–52, *52*
Williams, Bob, 51
Willis, Bill, 54, 55, 58
Wilson, Bobby, 43
Wilson, Marc, 79, 88
Wilson, Wildcat, 40
Wood, Willie, 71
Woodruff, George, 14, *15,* 17, 18
Woodson, Charles, 104
World Football League (WFL), 87

Yale University, 6, 9, 10, 12, 13, 14, 16, 17, 24, 26
Young, Buddy, 55
Young, Steve, 88, 95, 109, *109,* 112

About the Author

Mark Stewart ranks among the busiest sportswriters of the 1990s. He has produced hundreds of profiles on athletes past and present and authored more than 40 books, including biographies of Jeff Gordon, Monica Seles, Steve Young, Hakeem Olajuwon, and Cecil Fielder. A graduate of Duke University, he is currently president of Team Stewart, Inc., a sports information and resource company located in Monmouth County, New Jersey.